FIVE HOURS BEFORE MIDNIGHT

FIVE HOURS BEFORE MIDNIGHT

A Story of Fear, Faith, and Survival

Mary Adams

AMBASSADOR INTERNATIONAL
GREENVILLE, SOUTH CAROLINA & BELFAST, NORTHERN IRELAND

www.ambassador-international.com

Five Hours Before Midnight
A Story of Fear, Faith and Survival

ISBN:978-1-62020-271-5
eISBN: 978-1-62020-373-6

Cover design and typesetting: Hannah Nichols
E-book conversion: Anna Riebe

AMBASSADOR INTERNATIONAL
Emerald House
427 Wade Hampton Blvd.
Greenville, SC 29609, USA
www.ambassador-international.com

AMBASSADOR BOOKS
The Mount
2 Woodstock Link
Belfast, BT6 8DD, Northern Ireland, UK
www.ambassadormedia.co.uk

The colophon is a trademark of Ambassador

Dedication

To my husband, Arthur: thank you with all my heart.

Love, Angel

“Let Nothing Disturb Thee”

by Henry Wadsworth Longfellow and Teresa of Avila

Let nothing disturb thee,

Nothing affright thee;

All things are passing,

God never changeth!

Patience endurance attaineth to all things;

Who God possesseth in nothing is wanting;

Alone God sufficeth.

Contents

Don't let life consume you, don't

let it take the wind out of your

sails, life is a journey, one we

must all take. Be confident, be

sure, know that God is with you,

you're not alone. Make life count,

make it a victorious one, and you

too can leave a mark.

Confidence comes by trusting in God

Acknowledgments

Reaching back into the far corners of my mind, I search my life and I am still touched by memories. I tearfully reminisce about the many chapters gone by and anticipate the pages of unwritten works before me.

As memories come alive, my emotions begin to stir. Once again I open revelatory feelings of my heart. I am very transparent, an open book, a witness of the glorious grace of God.

Through the years, I knew the roads I had travelled were for a reason. Yet, no matter how hard those roads became, I knew the Lord was with me; I was not alone. My Bible, pen, and journals have played an important part in my life. When I flip through the pages, my pen begins to write, and I become more aware of God's awesomeness.

Never in my life had I ever imagined such victory. I can honestly say it has been one extraordinary adventure. As the chapters unfold, I am more grateful to the Lord for how far I have come by His grace.

As I sit in my garden, I am totally mesmerized by God's graciousness, love, and magnificent design of life. Surrounded by speckled finches chirping on the branches of the old willow tree over by the wishing well, my chubby, little cats play, running through the huge ivy bushes as they play hide and seek. I admire the colorful pallets of roses, which stretch across the little bridge nestled by the beautiful asparagus bush, I lose me in the beauty.

In the distance, on top of my red bottle brush tree, a magnificent dark-wing red breast songbird flutters its wings and sings—in high pitch—a beautiful melody that echoes through the brisk winter breeze. Totally captivated, I am lost in total peace and embrace the seasons of my life.

From where I once was to where I am today, God's love has brought me through under the shelter of His wings. I am victorious; all I am, and all I will ever be, I owe to Jesus.

Never did I think when I stepped out from under the rubble and ashes of my shattered life, I would achieve such victory. I count my blessings one-by-one and am forever grateful to God for His unfailing love, His abounding mercy, and His unchanging heart.

Chapters yet to be written, stories yet to be told—with the stroke of the pen—will once again outline the continued story of my life. Writing this story gives me another opportunity to bare my soul. Written between these pages are the feelings of my heart. After all these years, I can wholeheartedly say God has certainly been good to me.

Be encouraged to not let fear consume you; do not let your past cripple you. No matter what road you have travel, no matter how hard your journey may be, God's best awaits you. The best is yet to come. You, too, can be victorious and leave a mark.

Many thanks to my husband, Arthur, for the endless love and support you gave me. To my daughter, Mimi—for always being there—thank you. To my dear friend, Susan Sorian: once again for your love, dedication, and loyalty in the rewriting of my book. To all my little buddies, I appreciate your love and companionship. Brenda Castrejon, thank you for your faithfulness and friendship. To my publishers, Sam and Tim Lowry, thank you for believing in me once more.

I extend my heartfelt thanks to you all.

Prelude

Twenty-five hundred miles from the only home I had ever known, I desperately pushed against all odds to make a new life in California. Mistake after mistake was made as I fell into traps; life seemed to hit me from all sides. The more I fell, the deeper I descended, each time.

I had fallen into another horrific relationship—far worse than the one I had with T. J. Masterson. I ran with every ounce of strength within me from the shadows of my past. Regardless of how hard I ran, I seemed to lose my footing. I fell back into the hands of the devil.

Fear consumed my mind, body and soul. It was fear that stripped me of my senses and caused me to run for my life. When I faced my fear head-on, I knew I could not lose control; I had to survive. I gave the devil a run for his money.

Three days from nowhere, I felt trapped in a dark, cold, and isolated tomb where I struggled to find my way out. The eerie stillness of night's blackness scared me as if death stalked me. I was frightened out of my mind and felt someone was walking over my grave.

With nowhere to run, nowhere to hide, I was surrounded by death as I fumbled in the darkness. I fought to maintain my sanity. I earnestly prayed and knew God had not forgotten me.

After a dark and horrible night that almost ended my life—one of the scariest I had ever encountered—I counted my blessings to be alive. After I experienced that horrid feeling, which pierced my entire being, I realized I was a long way from getting my life right.

Thank God, someone watched over me. Survival took on a whole new meaning because of that horrific period in my life. I became more determined to get things right. A new sense of *me* had arisen; a complete transformation of mind, body, and soul happened. It was like I had been born again.

That period was blistering and ruthless. Unwritten chapters lay dormant and weighed heavily on my heart. Pages of sheer nothingness compiled as I live out that horrific season. I knew my fear could not control me; I had to survive and not allow fear to consume me.

God gave me beauty for ashes. With every ounce of faith within me, I pushed forward and ultimately became victorious.

I pray my story blesses you. I pray the souls that have lost fight and each broken spirit, know this: you are not alone. The very roads you have travelled have been travelled before. Chapters have already been written by the stroke of someone's life pen. Those crazy, heartfelt emotions and insanity of mind have been experienced by many before you.

Yes, I, too, have experienced lunacy. So, stand fast and take heart. Trust in God. He will give you beauty for ashes. I bare witness of this truth—with God all things are possible.[1]

1 Matthew 19:26, New International Version (NIV)

CHAPTER 1

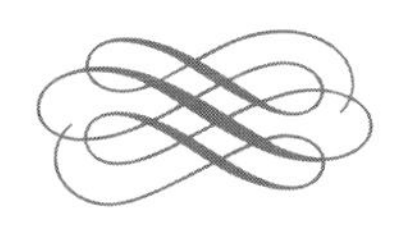

Reluctant Heart

Winter arrived as the grey skies overtook the fields and countryside while the tall barren trees stood lifeless in the cold, blistering noonday sun. From season to season life spoke; its grandeur and loveliness were a masterpiece of divinity and art.

I took great joy as I embraced a life for which I was truly grateful. I thanked God for being alive and the opportunity to be part of His magnificent design.

I had a chance to shine light into the darkness as I shared the experiences of my life with others. I have explained that no matter how long a road may be, or how hard a challenge may appear, to never give up. Wherever we are, the Lord has already been and wherever we are headed, He is already there. I pray my life experiences held up as a cautionary tale, perhaps becomes a message to bless someone in need.

As I sat in my bedroom, nestled between the folds of my quilt, I was lost in the peace that surrounded me. I took in the stillness and quiet of the night. What a simple delight it was to sit in my blue tapestry chair and look over the field.

I admired the coral haze as the sun began to set. It stretched over the mountaintops and made a beautiful addition to an empty canvas. Its rays brought to light the splendors of God's creations.

All sort of thoughts about my childhood raced through my mind; emotions of all kinds roused within me about pages of unwritten stories and years of fear and isolation. My thoughts awakened my soul and stirred feelings locked at the bottom of my heart. I stared into the cold, windy night and saw my reflection on the picture window beside me. It reminded me of who I once was—a terrified little girl, who was rejected and misunderstood—and who I am today—the confident woman God intended me to become.

I thanked God for loving me; His faithfulness gave me beauty for ashes, and raised me above the ruin and rubble of my shattered life. Those thoughts, memories, and emotions loomed in the recesses of my heart like blocks of coal became jewels awaiting their time to shine. I had come to realize they were all part of me, the tapestry of my life that God intended to use for His glory and to bring hope to others.

In everyone's estimation, my life was worthless. I never knew why my mother rejected me, allowed others to abuse me, or prohibited my father from caring for me. What had I done for her to lock me away in a room or an attic and send me away for years at a time?

With only the company of nuns at a convent and children, who would ultimately leave when they were adopted to live in loving homes, I had no companionship, no comfort.

I did not know God loved me through and in spite of it all; He had a plan for my life. I did not know He waited to meet me with a love greater than any human love I had ever known. Yet, I learned I would never have to walk my journey or face uncertainties alone because God was with me. Through the seasons of my life, the Lord has never failed me. Our God is an awesome God. He's a God of restoration and more than enough.

I sat among the many treasures God had given me—my mind, soul, and heart. All He had restored back to me. I was a broken pot cast down, forgotten and left for dead by the very ones who should have loved and protected me. It was the only world I had known and come to love, yet it had been taken from me. I was left to drown in my tears. The Lord put me back together and made me whole. He brought peace where turmoil was housed and courage where terror had resided.

I cuddled up within the folds of my fluffy, white, flannel quilt. I heard the winter winds blow fiercely through the tall barren trees as dried up leaves fell from its branches and drifted in the wind. My chimes began to ring to make such beautiful melodies. It was as though the night winds and chimes played a symphony.

I enjoyed a hot cup of tea, surrounded by peace. I flipped through the pages of my mind and reflected on God's goodness. I was amazed at what God had done for me. Through the thunder and lightning, another season came to mind, another time of my life was visualized.

On May 8, 1982 a new beginning started for me as I stepped over another threshold in time. I was caught between an unsettled heart and the insanity of uncertainties around me. God knew I had to push on. Although more pages waited to be written, my pen was anxious to write. Ever so carefully I watched my step and did not allow my impulsiveness, or my lack of patience, to get in the way of the destiny God had for me.

As I sorted through the pages of time and focused on moments in my life—those little treasures of my heart—that I truly wanted to share it with you. As complex as my life may have been, I did not want to reveal all of me; yet, there is so much to share.

I searched my inner self, and God revealed chapters, which can be a true blessing. Perhaps, these stories can make a difference in someone's life.

As I listened to the rain fall I conjured a mental portrait of me for you, the reader, to envision. In 1978, my life was so disconnected. I was the mother of four children—Cody, Casey, Bobby, and Mimi—who were products of a broken home. I had been abused, burned bridges, and my family was scattered all over the place.

My children had been stolen from me by their vengeful father and grandmother, which left a huge void in my life, my soul. My ex-husband, T. J. Matheson, was used to having things go his way. With an obsession to own and control me, he was sent into a fury when I divorced him in 1975. I was forced to go on welfare because the financial strain to care for me and four children was overwhelming. We had settled into a three-bedroom cold-water flat in a seedy district.

To make matters worse, I had no high school diploma. Yet, in spite of all the odds stacked against me, I was determined to get off welfare. I needed to secure a job to make a better life for my family. In January 1976, I got a job driving school buses; shortly thereafter, I started driving charter buses.

However, my ideas for my future and my mother's ideas were quite different. Like T. J., she also wanted control of my life, which created conflict between the two of us.

"Quit your job, Mary, and go back on welfare so you can stay home to raise your children," she insisted. "If you don't, you'll be very sorry."

She hoped against hope that T. J. and me would reconcile. Well, after two years of failing to try to control me, she made good on her threat. Together, she and T. J. ripped my world apart—they took my children.

I was left on the outside looking in, as I had no money to hire a lawyer. I could not go to the police because T. J. had a relationship with police personnel. I felt defeated. However, I knew that situation was not permanent. I did not know when, how, or where, but I knew God would make wrong right.

My fifteen-year-old son, Cody, escaped with me from Orange, New Jersey to Southern California. Cody was the spitting image of his father and a strong-willed teenager. He was in a rebellious stage and angry with his father for abusing me. As a result of the beatings, name calling, and ongoing fights Cody had witnessed between my husband and me, he showed no love toward his father. In turn, T. J. had built a wall between himself and Cody—he rejected his son.

I was armed with little more than bus fare, desperation, and a determination to start a new life for me and my children. I did not know what the future held. I had experienced a year of unsettled fear and emotions. Miles from the only home I had ever known. I did my best to pick up the pieces of my life.

I feverishly tried to put together something that had completely shattered at my feet. I prayed some of the scattered pieces were repairable, but only God knows the outcome of a challenging task. Hope was all I had left, along with my faith and trust in God. I hoped my children and I would be reunited.

Aware of the possibilities set before me, I had to put my thoughts back on track; calm down; and, most importantly, not step ahead of the Lord. My feet were planted firmly on the ground and my eyes were focused on the cross. I refused to let my past cripple me and ignored the odds stacked against me. I stood fast on God's promises and stopped me from jumping off the edge.

After years of living life my way, I gave the Lord the reins. Soon after, doors opened and hope surfaced within me about a new start. Filled with great enthusiasm and excitement, I ran with it. There was so much to explore, so much ground to cover. I stood in uncharted territory, took a leap of faith, and continued to run my race.

A thin line between sensibility and impulsiveness became apparent. I had to keep my mental state in tact; failure was never an option for me, even though I had setbacks. I was more determined than ever to make my life the best it had ever been.

My mistakes had become learning tools. The years of tears had worked together for me. I knew, beyond a shadow of a doubt, I was going to achieve those goals God had placed in my heart. I wanted a new and stable home, a united family, and more confidence. I knew I would complete the journey God had for me.

After I had experience years of self-doubt and insecurity—my internal war—I regrouped and began to date Eric Richards, a deacon at the church I attended. Eric was smooth talking and very charming. He was someone who seemed to have his life together. This man had it all and swept me off of my feet.

We spent weekends at Catalina Island on his boat, dinners at West Hampton, and so much more. Every day seemed to be a holiday; I was showered with gifts and the situation seemed as if I had walked into a dream. I was caught up in wondrous bliss and started losing touch with reality. My mind was clouded by the lifestyle he had shown me. He was an heir to a small fortune, a successful investor, and a musician. My judgment was lulled by the sweet words he had spoken to me.

Many nights my inner conscience reminded me everything that shines is not gold. Torn between reality and fantasy, I had to catch me before I lost my identity. The relationship had begun to develop in ways I had not anticipated, and I felt I was losing control. Things were moving way too quickly; beyond a normal pace.

Eric began to exhibit signs of jealousy and wanted to control my life. He would call unexpectedly to check up on me, show up where he was not invited, and made me feel smothered and fearful. The situation was crazy and I came to my senses.

God help me, what am I doing? I thought.

I wanted to be loved and a desperate change of direction was needed to get to where I wanted. I had to develop great discipline, not nurture a crazy, emotional state-of-mind. I knew if I did not get a grip, I would have become lost in the fast lane, headed for self-destruction.

The craziness of every day life can cause one to get caught up in a vicious cycle. If the person does not watch the road signs, his or her life can turn into an irreparable catastrophe. God knows the many cycles in which I had trapped myself because I had made many bad, rushed decisions. They were fueled by a fear that life was passing me by.

I experienced knee-deep and over-my-head chapters in my life from being abused to allowing me to be used to entertain and provide pleasure to others. I had become a slave to my deceptive feelings of worthiness.

I had become concerned for Cody's safety, so I sent him back to New Jersey to live with his grandmother. God knew there were times when I should have been dead, but by His grace, I lived through all of it. It is only because of His love and divine mercy that my journey continues today.

In March 1984, a year and a half after I sent Cody back to stay with my mother, I moved into my bachelorette apartment in El Segundo, California. For the first time in a long time I was my own person! My apartment was a quaint little place with a brick fireplace in the corner and a cozy little dining nook nestled between the alcove of the kitchen and the foyer.

It was my little place, my sanctuary, a place where I was lost in the quietness of the eucalyptus trees and huge pine trees that grew outside my bedroom window. My humble abode was far from the hustle and bustle of everyday life. Within its walls, I had cried an ocean of tears, for many periods had gone by without closure—unresolved.

As I sat, looking out my bedroom window, I embraced the newness of life. God had certainly been good to me—for once in my life I had stopped to smell the roses. I heard the song birds sang. At nightfall, I enjoyed the stillness of evening.

As my old classic music took me away to the better seasons of my life, I pondered about how I had waited so long for such a moment. I guess the horrific chapters of what my life used to be helped to build my character; they made me strong. Every splinter of the cross embedded in my shoulders and made me more determined to run my race.

I had decided not to let my mother or T. J. gain any control of my life. It was my life, and having only one life to live—come hell or high waters—no one was going to stop me. I was going to be victorious. A new chapter was about to begin and unaware of what's before me, I knew it was difficult to bare my soul. It was hard to open up to anyone because I was reluctant to reveal the feelings of my heart.

"Mary, give me a chance. I won't hurt you," Eric insisted.

I hung on his every word and tried to stay afloat. I did not want my feelings to run away from me.

"I'm not T. J. I'm not like him. Please believe me," he said.

I was torn between my yesterday and that chapter being written; cold stillness ensued. I was stuck between what had been and where I was.

God, I don't want to make a mistake again.

There had been many broken promises, many empty words, and many dead dreams. God knew I guarded my heart. I could not allow my feelings to run away, so step-by-step I allowed me to fall in-love again.

May 1982 arrived and Mother Nature was actively in full bloom everywhere. Near my kitchen windows sparrows made their little nest. They fluttered their little wings and picked up all sorts of twigs and leaves from under the huge eucalyptus tree next to my bathroom window.

Spring is a time of new birth, a time to regroup. I thought my thoughts and was able to catch my second wind. Many warm spring nights I called home to speak to my little family, but many of my calls were fruitless. Unfortunately, neither my mother nor my son, Cody, wanted to speak to me. After I sent Cody back to New Jersey, my mother convinced him I did not want him.

It is remarkable and unbelievable how nothing seems to change. That chapter of my life seemed a never ending saga. My mother and I remained worlds apart. My ex-husband still made life hard for me. New Jersey seemed centuries away.

I had seemingly morphed into another dimension, one where the past no longer existed. Far from where I started, I wanted to somehow create a bridge to connect my past and present. My world had crumbled, yet had been elevated to the new life God had given me. A task God, and God alone, could make happen.

Lord it's hard for me to comprehend why You'd send shy, timid little me so far away. I'm confused because these roads leave no mark; I see nothing I've accomplished. God, help me to make this right. I can't lose again, I must win.

Within the circle of life I had to fit in. My pen eagerly awaited a chance to write about my new chapter in life. To fill in blank pages to continue my life's story. Life was so complicated; I seemingly wandered in the dark, miles from nowhere.

"Mary, are you listening to me? Are you listening to anything I'm saying?" Eric asked.

His words sounded the same. My heart was very reluctant; I was so afraid of giving my heart away. I wanted love, I want to be loved, but feared I would awaken to find our relationship was a continuum of mine with T. J. Masterson.

What do I do . . . What do I say? This man is trying, but I'm not. I don't want any ties or commitments yet.

"Mary, please give me a chance. I won't hurt you," Eric pleaded.

Those words taunted me and were repeated in my head. I felt nothing—not toward him, but myself. Perhaps, my heart guided itself, my entire being entombed in a period deep inside me. Past shadows haunted me like chains that held me down.

I'm chained to the past, dear God, so what's to become of me? Lord, will my mother and T. J. win? Help me, Lord. Please, please help me!

Although across the country, T. J. and my mother still haunted me. I was overwhelmed by a feeling of nothingness invoked within me. Their actions made me feel so unworthy of love.

I must climb out from under the hold they seem to still have on me and begin to live again.

I have heard it said when one door shuts another door opens. I stood on the threshold of what once was and yet to come. My past awaited my failure, my great fall.

Well, hell will have to freeze over before I'd give into them. Come hell or high water, I will be victorious.

I had walked through valleys and crawled over dry scorching deserts. I had walked through uncharted territories. Yet, I was still alive—the devil was not able to take me out.

God had a purpose for my life, even though I could not see it. I knew without a doubt, He held my life in the palm of His hands.

Months passed and I kept up the pace, after I had gotten a job as a bus driver, to work hard to save money as part of my plan to bring my little family out to California. Eric and I were still seeing each other; things between us seemed good. In fact, he was once again the charming man with whom I had originally fallen in-love. I began to think he was the answer to my future.

As busy as I was, my reluctance to repeat the past left me torn between what I perceived and what I had actually experienced—my emotions were wild. I was so caught up in my emotions, I was unsure of reality. It was a battle of my mind, a private war.

Many nights I tried to find peace to sooth my restless soul. I wanted to get things right, yet I still had a lot of unresolved issues to settle. Most important were issues with my family. I did not want to go through life bitter and with a hateful heart. I did not want to take my journey with a negative attitude.

My greatest desire: to leave a mark. I wanted my life to count for something. As I anxiously awaited my turn, I prayed with expectancy. The blank pages of my life remained without content, but I prayed they would express the feelings of my heart.

I anticipated the outcome of my journey and believed the roads I travelled would reveal God's bigger plan for my life. Until such revelation, that chapter being written had to be lived as I moved toward chapters to come.

CHAPTER 2

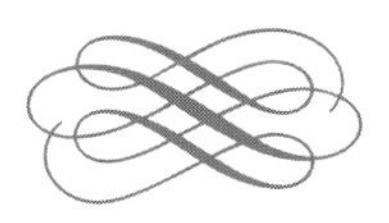

Forget Me Not

I embraced another new day. Everywhere I looked, life was a magnificent and delightful treasure of God's hand in motion. From where I was seated, I saw tall, barren trees—marred by a cold winter—begin to bud as tiny sparrows sat on branches. They fluttered their wings and basked in the noonday sun.

The world was simply gorgeous. God's creation of life is exceptional; His love is expressed in fine detail. How wonderful to be a part of His splendid design. Everything changed so dramatically, but my life seemed to remain the same. Every time I reflected on the mistakes I had made, I sobbed.

The brokenness I had experienced in New Jersey—the world that had been taken from me—was one of my biggest nightmares; marrying T. J. Masterson only added to its horror. I was the catalyst for the downward spiral into my life of abuse and despair. I had to work hard to get my family back.

It had been over a year since I had moved to El Segundo, California; I really tried to get things right. Many chapters still needed to be written, many stories still needed to be told. Secrets resided within me, yet I knew my pen would draft the remaining stories of my life.

Confused and grieved with sorrow, I awaited my miracle while I was in no-man's land. I tried to figure out how to undo all the wrong that had been done and realized picking up the pieces of my life was not easy.

How do I reconstruct what's been shattered and torn apart?

I had so much work ahead of me and so many stones yet to roll over. As each day passed I took one step toward getting my life right. I did not let anger control me because I did not want to become bitter. I definitely did not want my past to cripple me.

The challenges set before me were an enormous proportion, which mounted to extraordinary heights. Yet, regardless of the magnitude of those challenges, I knew I must move forward, I must press on.

At thirty-something, my mother and T. J. still wanted to control my life. The transcontinental distance had not mitigated the craziness around me. God kept my sanity. The heart-wrenching years gone by only made me more determine to reach the finish line. I had come too far to turn back.

Although those episodes seemed never-ending, I was too stubborn to stop. Angry or not, it was all on me; if I lost control, then T. J. Masterson won after all. I was at another threshold in my life and looked into the future. The pages began to turn; I wanted to ensure I crossed all *T's* and dotted all *I's*.

It was a beautiful warm night; the day had finally come to a close. As I indulged the peacefulness around me, I sat on the veranda and called back home.

"Hello," my mother said.

"Hi, Mom, it's me. How are you? How's Daddy? I miss you all," I replied. "How's Cody doing?"

I choked back tears because I did not want my mother to hear the brokenness of my heart. I feared she would rebuke me.

"What do you want? You call after all this time . . . What the hell happened? Did you forget you have a son!" my mother shouted.

"Mom, please talk to me. I miss you," I begged. "I'm your daughter. Please, Mom, just talk to me."

"What daughter? My mother died at thirteen; I don't have a daughter," she replied and then the telephone clicked.

Oh, she angers me so! That woman just tears my heart apart. Why she takes pride in hurting me, I'll never know, I thought. *I never knew a mother can hate her child. Here I am, so far away from home, and she acts like I never existed.*

Once again I had been catapulted into the midst of absolute nothingness. My mother and I were still worlds apart. Distant and time did not seem to mean a thing. It seemed so hopeless.

How do I make something out of nothing?

I sat wrapped in my pain, cried my heart out, and wondered if my life would be better if I never returned home again. Time had escaped me, even the sounds of the night started to fade to nothing, but a silent hush. It was so quiet I heard my heartbeat.

When the lights in the courtyard started to dim, I got up and walked inside. I made a cup of tea and lay across my bed to pray. Suddenly, the telephone rang.

"Hello," I said.

"It's me, Mom," Cody replied. "Grandma wants to talk to you."

He handed the telephone receiver to his grandmother.

"Mary, T. J. has been calling. He's furious because you left New Jersey and is causing all sorts of problems!" my mother shouted.

"Mom, tell him to call me. Something's got to give."

"I should've killed you years ago. Even this part of your life you can't get right!" she yelled, and then she hung up the telephone again.

Those ugly, repetitive seasons continued without any answer. T. J. had made it up his mind a long time ago to make my life miserable. He had succeeded and it appeared he was not going to stop until he had destroyed me.

That crazy, vicious cycle had to end. I was determined to not let T. J. get the best of me nor allow his craziness to destroy me. He played mind games and had messed with my mind long enough. I needed to get tough and fight back.

Eric and I started dating on a more frequent basis. That chapter of my life seemed so exciting; he was like a breath of fresh air. Every opportunity I had to free me from the past, I took. I wanted to break the chains that held me in bondage and get on with my life. I refused to let the cruel, harsh years of long ago stop me.

My spirits were high and passion flowed through my veins. I wanted to break out from under, to be freed from T. J. Masterson once and for all. By staying in the fast lane, time slipped though my fingers. I stayed busy to keep my mother's hurtful words off my mind.

"Mary, I love you," Eric said.

Love: a small, four letter word that was supposed to mean so much. However, it actually meant nothing—question upon question, idiocy, and emptiness void of meaning. T. J. Masterson did a number on me. Whenever I heard the words *I love you,* I withdrew and ran.

How do you give love when you weren't shown love?

The only genuine love I had ever felt was my daddy's love. My mother was the one in control when I was growing up. In spite of his best efforts, my father was never allowed to rescue me, aside from removing me from our home. I knew he loved me, but he was prohibited from fully expressing it.

When I left New Jersey, my mother shut the door on our relationship and any form of communication with him. As a result of that experience, I was scared to let go and love again.

Eric and I seemed good together, and we went everywhere. It was quite difficult for me to accept the events, which led to our relationship progression. I did not really feel free to show my feelings toward him. It seemed as though something tugged at my heart. Confused and very uncertain, I had mixed emotions and hated feeling the way I did.

No matter how hard I tried to not bring my past into my present, those negative, itsy-bitsy internal twitches managed to surface. They prevented me from moving forward into a space of love in my life. I was frustrated, aggravated, angry, scared, and wanted to pull my hair from its roots. Regardless of how I looked on the outside, my insides boiled over.

"Mary, give me a chance. I'm not T. J." Eric insisted.

As much as I wanted to believe him, I could not. It was much too soon to let my guard down. It had been quite some time since I had allowed a man to get close to me. I did all I could to keep a safe distance. Eric, a man who seemed so real, so good wanted to come into my life, my world and become a part of me. It scared me to death.

"Eric, I'm not ready yet. Please be patient," I replied.

He was so calm and seemed as though he understood me.

Time after time he would say, "Mary, I have all the time in the world. I'm not going anywhere."

Surrounded by the beauty of the night and the soft sounds of the evening, I heard dogs from afar. I heard the rustle of bushes where the cats loved to play. I was seemingly in another world, free from the heart-wrenching chapters of my life. No worries, tears, or fear, just feelings of a gentle, soothing, and peaceful time where there existed only me, no one around to hurt me.

I occasionally escaped into a world: an earlier memory my life. In my mind's eye, I went back to Essex Avenue in Mama's attic. I cuddled between the folds of old, brown, woolen army blankets stacked by the fireplace with Miss Molly in my arms. Sporty Beagle lay at my feet as he listened to the rain hit against the windowpane. I dreamed my dreams.

Those years of pigtails and ribbons, and songs that were sung, were very much alive within me. I was truly grateful to God for those few precious memories that cushioned overwhelming seasons of my life. Whenever I relived such moments, I became lost in those years. I lay for hours and time seemed to escape me.

I was lost in the stillness of the evening and had a chance to meditate. I reflected on my life, which had been complex.

How can I expect anyone to understand me? How can I bear the truth?

For fear of being misunderstood, I only wanted to reveal the part of my heart that did not disclose too much of my story. I hid little secrets. The many secrets of my life remained concealed as I embraced my inner child, who wanted to be free to love and be loved.

"Mary, I love you. I want to make you happy, so give me chance. Time will tell," Eric reasoned.

That man always seemed to say the right words. The tone of Eric's voice brought such calm and his entire persona made me feel at rest. A part of me wanted to give our relationship a chance, but a part of me fought back.

Internal wars and mind games were deeply embedded within me—a direct result of years with T. J. Every time I wanted to be set free, my bitter past grasped my heart. Somehow, those destructive tactics became engrafted within me and hindered me from going on with my life for fear of being hurt again.

Life quickly moved on and kept me in the fast lane, but I needed a break. I needed some time away from the hustle and bustle of everyday life, so I took a ride to the mountains one weekend. Everything was so beautiful—it was a breath of fresh air. I was lost in the laid back, serene atmosphere.

I took a horseback ride on a wooded trail by the creek. I also took a hike to Millers Pond by an old saw mill and even pitched a tent under a beautiful, starry sky. I enjoyed Mother Nature as the night sounds called out. It was good to be me.

I had a chance to get away from the craziness, nonsense, and never ending vicious cycle. I stepped back into my little world: a place where no one could hurt me or make me cry. I lay under night's beautiful, starry sky and gazed at the full moon to admire its brilliance and beauty. I wished on a star for my life to be better.

I moved on to a new chapter, the second time around. I tried to get me together and enjoy that part of my life. I looked down into the gully and saw tall evergreen trees clustered together. The scene captured such a beautiful picture of a familiar sight. My eyes beheld it and I was transported back to early years of Daddy and me.

As we climbed up the snowy hill my little feet slipped.

"Daddy, I'm falling," I cried out.

"I got you, Cockroach. Daddy's here," he replied.

On top that big, snowy hill were clusters of pine trees. With an axe in his right hand, Daddy hiked as a rope hung from the side pocket of his old gray khaki pants. Sporty Beagle tugged at that rope, which unraveled and fell on the ground. Miss Molly was wrapped in my arms, snuggled close to my heart while I clung to Daddy's pant leg.

Daddy cut down the most beautiful Christmas tree. When we returned home, it stood proudly in the center of our parlor. It brightened the room as a beautiful orange and yellow fire was fanned into flames while Christmas music played. My daddy had been the love of my life—another part of my life ripped from me.

One vengeful man's hatred toward me had destroyed that world. I was left with memories of what used to be. Flipping through pages of such seasons—yellowed, tattered pages faded by the passage of time—made me withdraw. Those clippings and treasured memories still brought tears to my eyes.

At thirty-something and twenty-five thousand miles from home, I restarted my life. Many questions raced through my mind as Eric Richards seemed to appear.

Why does my heart keep tugging at me? Why am I so afraid?

T. J. had left a bad taste in my mouth because of his deception. I did not know who to trust or what to believe. Everything that shines is not gold.

How does one detect a Dr. Jekyll and Mr. Hyde?

I finally returned home from my weekend getaway and retrieved numerous messages:

> Message #1 (T. J.): "Come home, Mary. You're never going to see the kids again! I'm not through with you yet. Getting away from me isn't as easy as you think!"

> Message #2 (Mom): "Mary, T. J. is furious. You'd better call; he's going to take Cody."

> Message #3 (Cody): "Mom, I want to come back to California. I don't want to live with him!"

> Message #4 (T. J.): "Mary, where are you! I've been calling. Did you fall off the face of the earth?"

T. J. remained relentless even miles away. His level of craziness continued: threat on top of threat. I refused to give into his demands, but that man was ego-tripping; he would not stop.

I needed to get that part of my life right. I needed God to help me and take things one day at a time. I did not give into another crazy cycle I had been trapped in for so long. I initiated a new chapter and new line. New words would be written until I got my life's story right. My faith kept me going until I won that fight.

Eric was very patient with me, but my reluctant heart kept me from opening up to him. I could not return the sentiments he desired. That part of me was closed off; I could not share me with him. I felt somewhat guilty as my heart was chained to those destructive seasons of my life. I was numb to the word: love.

Once again, Eric and I set sail to Catalina Island. Everything was beautiful: the ocean was magnificent, the huge waves were white-capped and hit against the enormous rocks. It was simply breathtaking, a beautiful picturesque sight. Under the vast starlight sky, the ocean water sparkled like pear-shaped diamonds.

I sat in total silence and admired the beauty around me. I was at peace. The ocean breeze felt delightful as the current gently gave movement to our boat. I seemed to float on air and dreamt on the waters of the great Pacific. I felt so calm; my entire being was at rest.

"Mary, are you happy?" Eric asked.

"Yes," I replied.

What a memorable time. I had not been at rest in years. I did not remember if I had ever felt like that before.

I was lost and drifted into another world void of pain, fear, or tears. The chapters of my life seemed to move so quickly. It was like my life was on fast forward. Although I enjoyed Eric's company, he was in fourth gear. He turned those pages too rapidly for me, so I geared down that much more.

If only what I felt had penetrated my heart. I would have a whole new chapter opened to me.

Am I truly happy, or am I just longing to feel loved?

Loneliness can be a cruel master that takes over our minds, bodies, and souls. I could not lose touch with reality, I could not lose control. Two steps forward, two steps back. I stayed on the edge of uncertainty and was stuck between the chapters of then and the present.

T. J. Masterson had done a real number on me, even though he was miles away. I still bore the emotional scars of that heart-wrenching chapter of my life.

When Valentine's Day arrived, Eric had a surprise evening planned out for the two of us down by the pier. What a beautiful night: a romantic candlelight dinner for two, a dozen long-stemmed red roses tied with red satin ribbons, and a bottle of vintage Perrier-Jouët.

The evening was so serene, so calm. The two of us sat under the beautiful sky, sipped a glass of wine, gazed at the full moon, and admired the illumination of the moon's brilliance as it shone down on the darken waters of the Pacific.

Am I dreaming . . . Can this really be true? Has happiness really found me? Am I capable of falling in-love again?

I sat in my apartment surrounded by the stillness of the night and searched my heart for the answers. I knew my relationship with Eric was not a game; a man's heart was at stake. I knew the feelings of rejection and did not want to do to Eric what T. J. had done to me.

I was in the middle phase of my life as I sat by the crackling fire and reflected on who I had become. I embraced the life before me as I watched the yellow-orange flames flicker on the pieces of pinewood nestled in their metal cradle.

Time had escaped me and before I knew it, it was seven o'clock in the evening. I took a nice, long shower and made a cup of hot tea. I was getting ready for bed when the doorbell rang.

"Good evening, ma'am. These are for you," the florist said.

"Thank you," I replied.

I had received lovely Forget-Me-Not flowers. They were simply beautiful. The flowers were presented in a tiny pot wrapped in dark purple foil with a beautiful lavender satin bow tied around it. Attached to the bow was a note that read: *Love, Eric.*

Until that point, my life had seemed to play out in a short time, and I thought it was over. I had travelled twenty-five hundred miles to start anew and embraced my restart with an open mind and receiving heart. For all that had been and all that was to come, I was truly grateful to God for the second chance.

CHAPTER 3

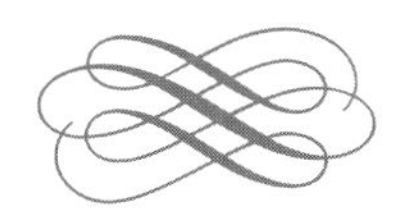

Penny Serenade

My days were very hectic. I worked twelve hour shifts and had very little sleep. It had taken a toll on me.

It had been a few weeks since I had seen Eric. Both of us had been extremely busy, and our lives had to be put on hold. In a sense, that was a good thing—I did not want to be rushed into a relationship. The time gave me more opportunity to recollect my thoughts.

Eric's birthday was around the corner, so he and his band (Fire and Ice) invited my girlfriends, Rosie and Jane, and me on a trip to Las Vegas for the weekend. It was absolutely exciting and thrilling. Dating Eric had taken me more places than I had ever dreamed of going. Yet, as excited as I was, my heart was still very reluctant and uneasy. Regardless, I made the trip out there.

When we arrived, the girls and I did some mall shopping; we must have walked around for hours. The lights, glamour, everything was showgirl style. I, too, was simply mesmerized. I had never seen such a theater of music and lights; the shows were simply spectacular. That entire evening captivated me—anyone would get lost in the glitter and lights of the city.

"Rosie, it's gorgeous here; it's simply beautiful," I said.

"You like?" Jane asked.

"Yeah, I can stay here forever," I replied.

All sorts of thoughts ran through my mind; one moment, I felt happy, but the next moment, I felt sad. I had unraveled, as if my emotions were on a rollercoaster. One day up, another day down; nothing seemed consistent.

From where I stood everything seemed out of my reach. For many chapters of my life, I was labeled with names I had chosen never to repeat. My entire life I had relinquished control of me to everyone, except me. I had been surrounded by negativity, which made me very angry, frustrated, and rebellious.

With Eric, I walked in the fast lane and wondered if it was worth the effort to convince my mother I was not the person she had labeled. The harder I worked at it, the more contemptuous she became.

"I should've killed you at thirteen. You're nothing, but a curse to me. Why I had you I'll never know. I should've killed you at birth," my mother said.

I felt tired and worn out. Being a good girl just did not seem to cut it. I wondered if I had been the opposite if she would love me any less.

At thirty-something I was experiencing a new chapter of my life—in the midst of all that craziness. I was going to live my life to the full. My mother and T. J. Masterson could either take it or leave it.

It was a gorgeous night in Las Vegas. The stars alone were magnificent and the entire sky was lit. It looked like a gala parade of lights. We walked on the strip for hours as we went from one casino to another.

Everyone knew Eric. In fact, we were treated like VIPs. Even the hotel where we stayed was luxurious; it was simply magnificent. From the velvet draperies to the plush, white carpets to the bathroom where gorgeous marble flooring, pedestal sinks, and wall-to-wall mirrors with gold lighting that surrounded the edges—it left me speechless.

Music played, candles burned, and the smell of jasmine accented the air. In the midst of the peaceful and serene atmosphere, I closed my eyes to indulge that moment in time.

Las Vegas was truly exciting. As I listened to Eric play, I was able to travel back to an earlier time of my life. I sat in the midst of all that beauty as tears filled my eyes. I ever so gratefully escaped the crazy world in which I had lived, if for only a moment. That moment seemed to last a lifetime to me.

How do I stop this madness, this crazy, vicious cycle between Mommy and me?

The more I dwelled on it, the more frustrated I became, and the the angrier I felt. The whispers of the past—visions of what could have been—were so painful, I was all messed up. My feelings unraveled, my heart was broken, my world was crushed, but I knew I was more than that.

God does not make mistakes. I had faith in God and was determined to take my life one day at a time. I prayed and believed the life I had been living would turn around. I would be victorious one day.

Time seemed to slip through my fingers. I had slipped light-years away. I remained wrapped in the songs that played; I escaped into my little world of dreams.

Candles burned to create such a delicate softness in the room. It was so beautiful my mind opened up to happier seasons of my life. For years, I had to be strong; I did not want to expose the truthfulness of my heart. I did not want anyone to see the brokenness. I did not want to be transparent to elements that would prey on my brokenness and destroy me.

At the stroke of midnight, I excused myself and went back to the hotel. I needed some time alone. As I walked in the foyer, I looked up at the magnificent crystal chandelier, and then heard: Dong! Dong! Dong!

The beautiful melodic sound reminded me of Mama's gorgeous, dark cherry wood grandfather clock. It stood in our foyer by the magnificent mahogany spiral staircase. The clock graced our home many a day on Essex Avenue.

I ran up the gold metal staircase to my room and placed my red sweater down on the green, marble table. I opened the drapes and poured a glass of white Chamblaise. I threw my body across the bed and allowed my mind to wrap around the beautiful, classical music that played on the radio.

Song after song played as the pages in my mind turned. I caught myself reminiscing about the past. I was seated in the midst of my brokenness, yet my mind enabled me to escape to happier chapters of my life.

The beautiful sounds of long ago called my name. They were echoes of chapters gone by, and opened me to precious melodies of the seasons of my life.

"I love you, Mary. My sweet, sweet, Mary," T. J. said as we danced under the beautiful starry New York City sky.

I thought I was in-love. We were teenage sweethearts, bobby socks and stockings, penny loafers, blue jeans, and black leather jackets! T. J. was one handsome young man. If the walls of that big, old Victorian house could talk, they would tell unimaginable stories—things of the past that meant the world to me.

"I love you, T. J.," I said as he and I sat under the white arbor, surrounded by Daddy's vintage grapes, and rocked back and forth on Mama's glider, dreaming our dreams.

At thirty-something with so much of my past within me, I walked back through the corridors of time. I was so happy to relive special moments whenever I wanted to go back home. Life continued to flash before me. Scenes of yesterday kept opening to me.

Even at my age, I could still revisit my home. I embraced the halls of that old Victorian house and allowed these chapters I once lived to come to life.

I relived enjoyable days of Daddy, Mommy, and me. The pathways opened in my mind. I saw me look out the big, bay window in our parlor as I stared at the beautiful meadow next to the old Presbyterian Church. The meadow was filled with daisies and wildflowers, reminding me of the many Saturday afternoons I walked through it. I picked yellow dandelions for Mama's shrine.

Mama was in the kitchen baking her delicious cookies and pies. Daddy sat on the front porch drinking mulberry wine and Sporty Beagle chased the old Derbyshire cat. In the midst of this beautiful scene I was lost in those beautiful years of Daddy, Mommy, and me.

As I fought my private war, I wanted to go back home, but I knew I could not. Going home would be a total disaster; the doors back there were shut to me.

How does one turn back the pages of time?

I choked up with tears over my shattered life and fell apart. Unturned stones, unresolved issues, and questions that may never be answered.

Will I ever have closure to those chapters gone by, or will they lay dormant in the deepest part of my mind?

Penny Serenade, collections from a shadowy past, little treasures, bits and pieces of the stories of my life. I could not let my emotions become engulfed within the seasons of time. My pillows were saturated with tears as the brokenness inside gave way to the feelings of my heart.

Will I ever be right? Will I ever love again? Is my destiny really awaiting me, or am I a passing stranger?

Music played as the candles began to dwindle. The wax continued to melt down the sides of the metal holders. In the midst of that peaceful, mellow evening, I had drifted light-years away. I heard faint echoes of the past call to me.

"Mary, come get these roses and help me carry them into the house," Mama called.

Fashionable, multicolor trellises filled with Mama's prized possessions. She went into the kitchen and pruned the roses she had picked. My little beagle wreaked havoc on the wicker basket stacked by the pantry door. Troubles, my little kitty, terrorized the fish. I stood and watched each scene unfold as I tied satin ribbons around the roses Mama picked.

Half-written chapters with yellow, tattered pages of seasons passed, sometimes cushioned the brokenness inside. Stuck between the past and the chapter being drafted, my life could not go on, but neither could it stop. More chapters needed to be written, more stories had to be told, and my pen yearned to write.

Since Eric Richards would be a part of some chapters, I needed to give life another chance. Hours passed, and I had lost concept of time. The clock on the nightstand next to the bed, read: 3:15 am.

Three days from nowhere, I was no good for anyone because I remained crushed under the chapters of T. J. and me.

"Mary, I love you, my teenage bride," T. J. said.

Why do those words haunt me? Why am I revisiting those seasons?

I lay across the bed and was filled with mixed emotions. I was so confused and uncertain about where my life was headed. I was broken, perplexed, and cast down; only God knew what had been best for me.

Much life remained within me, yet I had closed me off from the world. I did not want a commitment; a part of me did not want to fall in-love again. The question remained: where do I go from here?

While in this hotel room, I drifted light-years away. There was a big gap in time that kept me separated; something would not let me move forward.

Why does life hurt so much? Why do I feel so much pain?

I clung to my past. The little girl with pigtails and ribbons, and songs sung, was very much alive within me.

"Daddy, Daddy, have tea with me please," I begged.

Any opportunity I had to sit with Daddy meant the world to me. Mr. Bear, Miss Molly, Miss Annie, Sporty Beagle, Daddy, and me—we made a great team.

"Mary, are you all right?" Rosie asked. "You look funny . . . Are you all right?"

At a loss for words, I lay in total silence. In that precious world, those seasons of Daddy, Mommy, and me, I remained captivated. My mind was absorbed in the scenes that played before me. I was home.

The music continued to play as I heard echoes of the past call me. A strapping young seventeen-year-old boy sat on Mama's pear tree. He would completely turn my life around. A blushing fourteen-year-old girl was infatuated in that season and fell in-love with that young man. She never dreamed how the young man would change the course of her life.

As I flipped through the pages of my life, I smiled at the thought of those chapters gone by.

"Mary, are you all right?"

Someone's voice had interrupted my train of thought.

I abruptly responded, "What!"

What's wrong with me?

As I looked up, I thought T. J. stood over me.

"T. J.!" I said. "Oh, gosh, Eric, I'm so sorry!"

"Mary, what's wrong with you?" Eric asked. "You're not yourself."

I remained silent and could not answer him. Suddenly, a man stormed into the room.

"What's wrong, Eric?" asked Paulie, his drummer, as Eric stormed past him to exit the room.

"Her, she's what's wrong," he replied as he glared back at me. "I don't need this."

Suddenly, I was fired up. All those chapters of T. J. poured out of me.

"What's wrong with *you*? Have *you* lost your mind? *You* don't need this? Well, *I* don't need this either!" I shouted.

I wanted to get out of there; I did not want to stay any longer. The very thing I had tried to avoid—the ugly, vicious cycle I had left behind—seemed to replay once again. That familiar look and sound took me back to repugnant chapters of my life.

On the car ride back to Los Angeles, I stayed silent. My entire being shut down. That scene in the hotel room continued to replay: the ominous look on Eric's face, his eyes pierced right through me. I could not get that picture out of my mind.

God, I must stay in control. I don't need another disastrous relationship; a repeat of T. J. Masterson and me.

Music played. The soft, sweet melodies of days gone by had once again swept me into the midst of chapters of my life. Torn between the yellow, tattered pages of time, I felt homesick.

I sobbed and was broken inside. I so much wanted to hear my mother's voice and the smell of her sweet perfume. I wanted to see my father's beautiful smile as he played tea with Miss Molly and me. I wanted to see that big, old Victorian house with all its little treasures to which I was bound.

I want to return to those beautiful years of simplicity and innocence; the fragmented memories brought tears to my eyes. I knew I could not go home—I had no home to which I could return. That part of my life was gone forever. Like a fallen leaf on a cold winter night, I, too, had fallen into a state of nothingness.

As we made our way back to Los Angeles, I was in a dormant state-of-mind. I could only wonder if my heart, and my life, would ever be revived.

In a time and place away from where it all began, I was totally separated. A part of me was in California while so much of me remained in New Jersey. I knew I had to take back my life, gather up the pieces that were left, cut my losses, and move on. What once was, no longer existed; the chains which imprisoned me no longer ruled my life.

I needed to sort out which memories I would keep and discard those I had to leave behind. Although, I could not return home, I had tiny remnants of seasons for which I was grateful to have had in my life.

CHAPTER 4

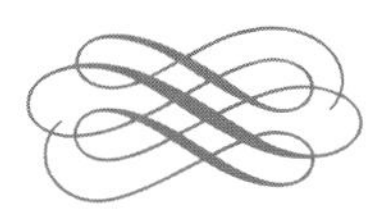

Mirror Reflection

Days moved on, and I had some extra time to spend with me, myself, and me. I was truly grateful for the chance to clear my mind. I had heard time healed all wounds; unfortunately, the reality of happily-ever-after simply did not exist for me.

Faded words on yellow, tattered pages discolored by the passage of time were thrown away in dusty trunks. They were remnants of seasons gone by: little reminders of the stories of my life. Once again I, through the middle of a new chapter of life where everything was so uncertain, so out of place, knew what I had experienced was real.

My heart ached for the familiar sound, faces, and places; I felt homesick. Those familiar sounds of yesterday, tiny swatches of years, haunted me and made me wish I could turn back the hands of time to change ugly chapters of my life.

In the midst of my brokenness, I had to move on. Life could not get the best of me; I had come too far to turn back. I could not allow my unraveled emotions control me. It was my life and since I had, but one life to live, I needed to stay confident. I had to complete my race.

I was not going to allow my circumstances to defeat me; the devil was not going to win. God had a purpose for my life and made no mistakes. Even though I did not see a light at the end of the tunnel, God sees the bigger picture. Because of that, I moved on to the other part of my life.

Two-thousand miles from where it all began and I was already victorious. That one big move certainly built my character. Because of that, I became the woman I was. God had not brought me that far to see me fall, so I firmly believed wherever life took me, I would prevail.

After that weekend in Las Vegas, I started to make changes. Perhaps I had jumped into something too quickly. After the years of T. J. and me, my outlook on life had changed. I tried to be cautious and thought twice before I made a move. Although Eric seemed nice, that night in Las Vegas left an awful impression. It was something that kept me wondering if I had moved too fast. Eric apologized a thousand times.

"I'm sorry, Mary. I'm truly sorry. It won't happen again," Eric pleaded.

What I saw did not make me feel good; that alone made me keep my distance. So, for the rest of the week I kept busy. I did all I could to ignore Eric's telephone calls. One night after work, Eric paid me an unexpected visit.

He presented me with a dozen long-stemmed red roses, tied with red satin ribbons; a five-pound box of chocolates; and a gorgeous pearl pendant.

"I'm sorry, Mary, please forgive me. It won't happen again," Eric promised.

Things seemed to get better; he did everything he could to please me. Although showered with gifts and attention, I still had reservations. We continued to date, and although everything was running smoothly, I insisted on my space. I wanted to take our relationship slow.

One evening after work, I had decided to take time out for me. I made a cup of hot tea, threw a few pieces of wood in the fireplace, and then pulled down the blanket to lie across the bed. For once in a long time, I relaxed. As the fire burned, I became sleepy; I curled up, pulled the blankets over me, and went to sleep.

I dreamed it was terribly dark—I could not see a thing. All I heard was heavy breathing. I was so scared and tried to run, but my feet felt heavy. I heard whispers I could not understand: chopped up words that made no sense.

"Who are you, and what do you want?" I cried out.

It was hard to breathe, and I perceived I was going to die. That heavy breathing grew louder, and I sensed a presence. I was so scared the tiny hairs on my arms stood up! Suddenly, in a panic, I woke up. My body was soaked in sweat and trembled.

I was so petrified I threw the blankets off and ran into the bathroom. My face was as white as a ghost's, and my hands were as cold as ice; I was falling apart. It was so bad I could not catch my breath. Suddenly, the telephone rang.

"Hello!" I gasped.

"Mary, are you all right?" Eric asked.

Before I could say another word, he hung up. Within minutes he stood at my front door. That dream shook me up pretty badly. I did not know if it was a sign, a premonition, or something more ominous.

I was not sure of anything. Perhaps, I was caught up in dreadful seasons of my past, but whatever it was. I took great notice and kept my guard up. I did not want Eric there; I felt very uneasy. In fact, for the short time he was there I had very little to say. I could not shake that dream.

Even though I tried to maintain some distance, he stuck to me like glue. I did all I could to avoid Eric. One Saturday evening, however, he popped up. He was very apologetic and handed me two dozen gorgeous long-stemmed red roses. He even brought dinner—a candlelight supper for two. We sat under the beautiful, starry sky on the veranda.

Everything went so nicely. In fact, later that evening we drove up to the mountains for the weekend. What a beautiful time we had during our log cabin style weekend. There was even a beautiful lake up there. Eric and I sat by the water while he played his guitar. Eric was in such a good mood; that man was really happy.

That entire weekend was lovely. Even Saturday night, he did little things to surprise me. We had a small campfire and Eric threw an old, brown, plaid blanket on the ground for us to sit on while he sang to me.

"Come on, Mary, relax. You look so tense," he commented.

My body had become rigid and stiff, like a twig ready to split in half. Why I felt that way, I did not know. All I knew was every part of me felt jittery. I anticipated jumping out of my skin.

"Mary, what's wrong?" Eric asked. "You're not yourself."

The thought of responding threatened me; I did not know what to say. I remained silent.

"Mary, what's wrong?" Eric repeated angrily.

I jumped at the sound of his voice. It was as though I knew something was going to jump out of the wall. I became scared and looked around, not knowing where I was. Fear really gripped me.

Everything had changed. Eric already detected the change in my demeanor, but he had also sensed a wall between us; in an instant, he changed, too. His facial expression shifted and he started to talk to himself. He became angry and actually self-argued. Ever so slowly, I started to walk toward the car.

"Mary, where are you going!" he shouted. "Come back here; you're not going anywhere!"

He got up and walked toward me, as he spoke loudly.

"Come here, Mary. You're not going anywhere!" he repeated.

I slowly walked backwards, hoping to get far enough away from him to run. I kept my eyes on him; he started talking to himself again. Twigs cracked and leaves rustled as I tried to move quietly. Yet, the earth beneath me did not cooperate due to dry debris underfoot.

In spite of the noise I made, Eric was not paying a bit of attention to me. I quickly turned and started to run. My heart pounded and I could not catch my breath. Death seemed to run after me. Suddenly, I heard his voice.

"Mary, Mary!" he yelled.

"I'm going to die, I'm really going to die, I know I'm going to die," I gasped.

I kept running. My legs were as heavy as weights. Nothing, but fear—ugly, overpowering fear—grasped every part of me.

"Mary, Mary, where are you!" he shouted.

I saw lights and what appeared to be a road ahead. I saw a tall figure.

Who is it?

I knew I had to run as fast as I could.

Maybe he can help me.

"He's gonna kill me, help me, please!" I cried out.

My legs felt funny; I could not go any further, so I dropped to my knees and sobbed.

"Are you all right, miss?" the stranger asked.

My body shook badly and I could not speak. I was so scared, everything about me fell apart. The man helped me up and took me to his car.

"Where are you going?" he asked. "Let me help you."

"L.A.," I replied through choked tears.

On the way to Rosie's and Bill's I did not say a word. I was so terrified. When I arrived, I jumped out of the car, ran up to the house, and rang the bell. When Rosie opened the door, I collapsed into her arms and cried. Later, Rosie told me the stranger who had dropped me off had driven off when she opened the door.

"Help me! Please, Rosie, help me," I gasped.

That night was disastrous; I had no answers and was truly beside myself. Eric had inadvertently shown me two sides of himself. On the one hand, he was charming and thoughtful. On the other hand, however, he was threatening and irrational. Eric had a split personality—he had issues way over my head. I knew nothing about him, but it was quite obvious there was something very wrong with him. I prayed because I knew only God could help me break loose from Eric once and for all.

When I looked into a mirror, I saw my reflection; what I saw truly troubled me. I looked so strange and desperately wanted to break from the chapters of my past. I did not want to repeat them. I did not know where to begin, but no matter how difficult it became, Eric Richards was definitely one person from who I had to get away.

The flutter of my heart, the spine-chilling sensation inside me, and repetitious chapters of days gone by, made me crazy. Those chapters haunted me and gripped my heart with horror—they frighten me out of my mind. Eric did not stop pursuing me. I did everything I to avoid his telephone calls. I even stopped going places we used to meet. No matter how hard I tried, Eric was relentless.

Months passed and everything had a new look. In spite of the changes around me, the East Coast remained the same. My telephone calls continued to be ignored, Cody became more arrogant, and T. J. became more out of control. The whole situation wore me down and chipped away at my emotional state. In fact, there were times when I had lost my wits.

My mind was so messed up, I could not think straight. My life was slipping away. Everything I had ever hoped for seemed to fade. I was a bundle of nerves and coming apart at the seams. My entire attitude had been affected.

Life was certainly challenging me. It got to the point where I was caught in a tailspin of a raging storm. I had to compose myself.

As the leaves began to fall from the branches of the eucalyptus trees over by my bedroom window, I decided to fight back and make changes in my life. I made up my mind that come hell or high water, my life was well worth the fight. Staying caught up in that vicious, never ending cycle my life would certainly self destruct. If I did not start somewhere, I would dwell as a prisoner of that vicious cycle for the rest of my life.

Eric kept calling. I continued to avoid him. Whatever Eric expected was not going to happen. The more I avoided that man, the harder he tried. I started to see traces of T. J. Masterson. One day I was leaving for work, and Eric was standing at my front door.

"Eric, this is not going to work," I said.

God knows it was not the answer that man wanted to hear. He exuded negativity: his silence and body language made me nervous. The look on Eric's face sent me years back in time. His silent stare, dark brown eyes that looked through me, raised lip, and arched eyebrow cast me into another dimension. I stayed at Rosie's and Bill's place more for fear of returning home.

God!

Everything spooked me. With the crazy hours I worked, I had much to fear. In the wee morning hours, I had to walk from Hawthorne Boulevard to my apartment. I was so scared and had no idea of Eric's whereabouts. Every time I worked a late shift, I was scared senseless. My skin crawled at the thought of Eric lurking somewhere in the shadows.

That man had left a bad impression—I was so beside myself that half of the time I did not know if came or went. I had paid a very high price for a very foolish and irresponsible time in my life.

I had another T. J. Masterson on my hands!

History had repeated itself twenty-five hundred miles away from the past, and I had foolishly gotten into another mess. I was fighting another war far worse than the one I had with T. J. Masterson.

Don't I ever learn . . . When will I ever stop?

The days got shorter. As the sun set, I would call home to speak to my mother. My family broke my heart. The reality of ever seeing them again grew dimmer. My telephone calls continued to be ignored, my letters were returned—any hope started to slip away.

Life became a hardship, things became more difficult to handle. In the midst of a broken heart, I sank deeper into my little world. I was torn between what I had hoped for and my reality. I felt like a wounded sparrow dying a slow death. Confusion and desperation had become my way of life.

Is returning to New Jersey my only hope of seeing my family?

Yet, I knew returning to New Jersey was not an option for me. So, I kept calling home and writing letters. I simply refused to go away.

More chapters needed to be written and more stories told. I knew I had to make it to the finish line, one way or another.

I reconsidered my thoughts and regrouped as I continued to strive toward the goal. At thirty-something, I should have known what I wanted. The reflection I saw in the mirror was a constant reminder of the foolish mistakes I had made and hasty decisions, which resulted in devastating effects on my family and me.

Waiting is hard, very hard, not to mention very painful. Patience has never been one of my strong attributes. I have always been impatient, but I have learned it is a great part of life. Like it or not, I have become patient.

After I stayed at Rosie's and Bill's for a while, it was time to return home. I hated being a prisoner in my life. I did not know why Eric threatened me, but something about him made my skin crawl. Regardless, I had to get on with my life.

When I arrived home, I took a long shower. Afterwards, I made a pot of herbal tea, dimmed the lights, turned on some classical music, threw myself across the bed, and relaxed for the rest of the evening. I experienced calmness.

From where I lay, the night sounds started to come in. Underneath my kitchen window, I heard the cats rustle through the shrubs, crickets chirp, dogs bark, and kids play hide-and-seek. My entire attitude changed for the better. I felt more relaxed and at peace, and as the hours passed, a bit sleepy. So, I pulled the white, fluffy quilt around me and slowly, but surely, went to sleep. I was suddenly awakened by pounding on my front door.

"Mary, open up; we need to talk!" Eric shouted.

I lay quietly, hoping he would go away.

"Mary, open this door now!" he continued to shout.

"Eric, go away before I call the police!" I shouted back.

I got up and ran over to the door to put the chain lock on. Then, I grabbed the telephone and called the police. I stood between the big brown leather chair and dresser in my bedroom. It seemed to be history repeating itself. So many memories ran through my mind: bad days between T. J. and me.

Oh, dear God, I'm back in Caldwell Hills! Back in those crazy heart-wrenching chapters of my life!

I felt like hell warmed over. Those horrible, spine-chilling, scary feelings of long ago overwhelmed me. It was like part two of *From Darkness to Dawn*[2] all over again. History had repeated itself. In no man's land, I dealt with another T. J. Masterson, but this time I did not know how to rid me of him.

Within minutes, everything was silent. I waited and then ever so carefully walked over to the kitchen window. I wanted to see if his black Camaro was still out front. As I peeked through the white-laced curtains, I saw the back of Eric's brown suede jacket get into his car.

Chapters turned, lines had to be written, and the pen anxiously awaited its chance to write, but I could not anticipate the outcome of that chapter in my life. Days were like weeks, and nights seemed to linger. The craziness seemed to have fallen off the face of earth.

However, I was not stupid. My gut feeling told me that chapter was far from over. I contemplated my every step, my every move to avoid entrapment by that madman. I spent a lot of time at Rosie's and Bill's as I worked and did nothing more. I kept calling back home, and finally one night I got through.

"Hi, Mom, it's me," I said.

She had very little to say. In fact, her tone was cold and dry.

"You have a son out here, Mary, or have you forgotten? You already lost your other three kids! Do you want to lose him, too?" she asked. "You've been nothing, but a curse. You should've died instead of your brothers."

My brothers, Michael and Anthony, had died during childbirth a year before I was born. A part of my mother died along with them. I guess her sorrow was so deep, she forgot about me.

---

2 Adams, Mary. 2008. *From Darkness to Dawn. Greenville, South Carolina: Emerald House Group Incorporated.*

Instead of being a blessing to her, her bitterness caused her to reject and deny me.

Tears ran down my face as I choked up; I stayed on the telephone until she hung up. Many of those telephone calls were three-sided conversations: my mother would always insert T. J. in the center of it all. Nothing changed; I remained on the outside looking in. I had such a heavy heart. Once again I was on my own. All I had was my faith in God and my will to survive.

Work kept me busy as I spent more time down at the bus transit division than I did at home. I drove the night owl shift on Line 40 (Hawthorne Boulevard and Martin Luther King, Jr. Boulevard). Many times I had to walk up 54th Street in the wee hours of the morning. It was so dark; some nights not even the stars were out. What made it even worse was when the low clouds set in, not even vehicle lights were visible.

I had jumped from the frying pan into the fire. Eric had become a complete nightmare to me. I was scared and my thoughts ran wild. I cringed at the thought my walk up 54th Street alone; it was one horrible experience. The night sounds alone sent eerie feelings up and down my spine; it took my breath away.

Death stalked me and that man was out for blood. The situation was overwhelming and drove me over the edge. My mind worked overtime and I grew tired of looking over my shoulder—Eric seemed to be everywhere. Dogs barked from afar, and sounds from bus air brakes on the boulevard were all I heard. I walked quickly and picked up my pace. I never knew where Eric was.

This chapter in my life was far different from the previous chapter. I was in a strange, unfamiliar area and uncertain about everything. Once again I had put me into a bad situation. I was in way over my head with no idea about the outcome, so all I could do was pray.

I managed to keep my sanity and my mind intact. I had not heard from Eric in a while.

Thank God, what was a relief!

Little by little I started to socialize with my friends; Bill, Earl, Rosie, Jane, and I went everywhere together. I had promised me not to jump at the first handsome face that came along and to not get entangled in any sweet words and with smooth talkers. My friends and I started to go back down to the pier to eat shell fish and drink white Chamblaise.

One night as we sat over by the rocks to watch the gorgeous waves come in, I heard an all too familiar sound of keys approach me from behind. The sounds of the rattle keys and coins jogged my memory. Right away I knew who it was.

"Mary, where have you been?" Eric asked with a sinister look on his face. "Have you been avoiding me?"

"What are you doing here, Eric?" I replied.

Suddenly, he grabbed my arm and pulled me toward him.

"Man, can't you see she doesn't want to be bothered," Bill, shouted. "I'll call the police!"

"Are you her spokesman?" Eric snapped. "Mary can speak for herself, can't you Mary?"

I was cold to the bone as chills ran up and down my spine. It was as though death had looked right through me. I slowly started to get up, but before I reached my feet, he grabbed me from behind and turned me around.

"Mary, don't mess with me," Eric said with a soft, spine-chilling calmness in his voice.

Bill and Earl got up and grabbed him.

Earl glared at Eric and said, "Leave Mary alone. What do you need . . . your senses knocked out of you?"

"I'll see you around, Mary," Eric said as he pulled away from Earl's grip.

My stomach was upset, my head pounded, and my hands shook uncontrollably. I sobbed.

"Mary, are you all right?" Rosie asked.

"Come on, Mary, sit down," Jane gently suggested.

"I can't believe this; it's happening again! I feel sick . . . Please, I want to go home," I cried.

Tears ran down my face, and my eyes burned. I sobbed and could not stop. All the way home I had flashbacks of exchanges between T. J. and me; crazy heart-wrenching episodes. I had gotten caught up in similar craziness again and wanted to hide, I wanted to run.

How did I allow this man into my life?

I thought I had my life under control and in check, but instead I was far from where I should have been. Somehow, I lost my footing. Because of that, history had repeated itself.

When I arrived home I was tired and exhausted; I felt totally drained. I grabbed a chair and sat down by the old steamer trunk by the fireplace. I grabbed a few pieces of wood and threw them onto the fire. I tried to unwind despite the hell I went through.

Overwhelmed by the situation, my eyes burned from tears and my throat was parched. I tried to find a solution to my hideous nightmare. So far away from home, far from familiar faces, I regarded me lost and alone. Many emotions ran through me; I had mixed feelings. Drained and totally wiped out, everything had become so senseless and nothing made sense to me.

My mind drifted back to the Caldwell Hills. Indeed, history had repeated itself. I should have thought enough was enough. I saw the days of T. J. Masterson and me replay in my relationship with Eric. I was at a total loss for words, but inside a war raged.

I was angry, disgusted, frustrated, confused, and bewildered. I perceived I was stupid because I seemed to never learn—I went from bad to worse. The feelings that tugged at my heart foreshadowed what was yet to come.

Instead of me leaving Eric alone, I opened me up to another disastrous chapter—a horrific, distorted, self-destructive one—with more complications and unsettled issues. It was something in which I had no business being involved.

Another setback, another giant step in the wrong direction; I went against my better judgment. As a result, I had another T. J. Masterson on my hands.

CHAPTER 5

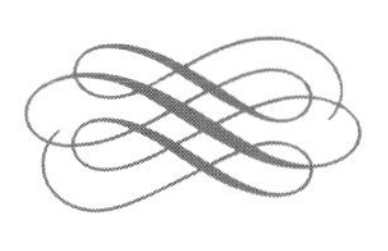

Crazy Cycle

Days moved on and I tried to regain some normalcy in my life. After that episode with Eric, I went through a lot of changes. I was mentally exhausted; my head seemingly doubled in size. My job kept me busy, which was a definite plus for me.

I gave great thought and consideration to taking a vacation since the company owed me eighty hours. I started to make plans to return to New Jersey for a visit. I jotted down everything on a paper I wanted to do and listed the people I wanted to see. T. J. was at the top of my list.

So many things ran through my mind and mixed emotions ran through me. After twelve long months, I returned back to that unsettled chapter of my life. I hoped and prayed I could get my kids back.

I lived between my job and Rosie's and Bill's home. I did not want any complications in my life, so day after day I went to work and came home. If I had any extra time in between, I called back home and spoke with my family. One Friday night I did just that.

"Well, Mary, did you get enough of California yet? You have a son out here or have you forgotten!" my mother shouted.

I finally had some good news to share with her, but she was so irritated with me, I could not get a word in edgewise no matter how hard I tried.

"Mom, I have a surprise, don't you want to hear about it?" I asked.

"Damn, Mary, all you think about is *you*. Your father and I are too old for your mess. God should have taken you years ago. Why I ever had you, I'll never know!" she shouted.

I choked back tears as those ugly, hateful words pierced my heart and drained life from me. That woman was never going to change. She was determined to keep a wall up between us.

My mother doesn't love me, let alone wanted me. So, why do I keep trying?

"Mom, listen please," I said.

With that, she hung up the telephone. I held the receiver in my right hand as tears streamed from my eyes. Once again I was left in complete brokenness, crushed by rejection and my mother's feelings toward me.

My journey has had its ups and downs; it certainly has not been easy. I have lost count of how many times I stubbed my toe and fell on my face. Yet, the one thing that keeps me alive is my will to survive.

Pages of unfinished work, bits and pieces of lost chapters of my mother and me, and frayed and tattered pages yellowed by the passage of time needed to be completed. In the far corners of my mind I had a lot of unresolved issues—story lines void of writing. In fact, I still heard the voices of days long ago, which echoed through the corridors of time. I held onto the earlier memories of my life: the happier chapters, precious seasons of my life.

I maintained positive thoughts about my trip. I had a lot to do, but, I had spare time, so the girls and I took in a show and had dinner at a cute café in Hollywood. We sat at white, metal bistro tables with adorable blue- and white-striped umbrellas to enjoy a glass of wine.

It had been some time since I had a night out; it seemed like my entire body shut down. Everything about me seemed withdrawn. I was emotionally spent and needed time to regroup. I needed time for me.

After days of hustle and bustle to get ready for the trip, I heard from Eric again.

"Where have you been, Mary?" he asked. "I've been trying to call you."

It was unbelievable. I thought after everything, he would have gotten the message. It was quite obvious he had not. I hung up on him; I had absolutely nothing to say. Hours after our initial exchange, the telephone rang off the wall.

Around four o'clock that afternoon I was at work. In fact, I was on my layover and had done everything as usual: closed the bus doors, lit the head sign, and sat in the back to gaze out the side window into the night. From a distance I saw the figure of a man in a brown suede jacket and blue jeans walk toward the bus.

God, it's him! What's Eric doing here? How did he find me?

The closer he got to the bus, the meaner he looked. All that gold around his neck shined through the darkness of the night. The blackness of his soul pierced through me.

"Mary, open up this door . . . We need to talk!" he shouted. "Open this door, Mary, don't make me hurt you!"

I did not answer him. I looked at my watch and prayed for time to pass. As I sat there passengers approached the stop.

I had very little choice. As passengers boarded the bus, eeriness stirred inside me. I felt very uncomfortable with Eric being on board. All he did was stare out the window into the night. As the hours passed, he continued to pay his fare and kept riding.

At about eleven o'clock that night, the eeriness worsened. At Crenshaw Boulevard and Park Place, Eric walked to the front of the bus.

"You haven't seen the last of me," he whispered into my ear.

He slowly turned and walked off the bus. Shocked and devastated, I perceived someone had walked over my grave. The tone of his voice; his cold, dark, stony eyes; his body language—everything signaled the devil stood in front of me.

Chills went up and down my spine. The hairs on my arms stood. As dark as the night was, Death seemed to hover over me.

Compose yourself, Mary. You have to get through this night.

I could not bring myself to go any further; I was all messed up. So, I called the dispatcher to ask to be relieved.

What a night that had been. I was burned; my mind, body, and soul were exhausted and wiped out. I got off the freeway at San Pedro Street and drove around to the back of the transit division to pull in. My eyes darted all over the place, looking for Eric.

The man existed in a twisted, distorted, unbalanced world—it petrified and devastated me. His was a heart-wrenching, mind-boggling world that consisted of monumental unresolved issues.

I dropped off my paperwork, and then headed to the telephone to call Rosie.

"Rosie, will you please pick me up? Eric's looking for me again," I cried.

"Mary, I'll be right there . . . Stay put!" Rosie replied.

I sat at the table in the far back, which faced the front windshield and stared into the night. I prayed Eric would not walk through the doors. Time seemed to drag its feet.

Rosie, come on!

Suddenly, a black Camaro pulled up front.

Oh, God no . . . It's him!

I quickly got up and ran into the locker room. I was scared to death. From where I stood I heard Eric ask the clerk what time I got off from work.

"No, please don't tell him I'm here!" I whispered.

"I'm sorry, who are you?" Bob asked.

"I'm her boyfriend," Eric lied.

"Well, then you should know what time she gets off," Bob stated.

The next thing I heard was rubber burning down the street.

This crazy cycle is never ending! What in the world did I get into?

I slowly walked back into the driver's room. No sooner did I get up to the clerk's desk to thank Bob when Rosie and Bill walked through the front door.

"Are you all right?" Bill asked. "Gee, you look as pale as a ghost."

I nodded my head yes.

"That guy looked crazy," Bob commented. "He had a menacing look on his face. In fact, when I didn't tell him when you got off, he became furious. He clutched his keys, made a fist, and pounded the counter in a fit of rage, and then stormed out."

I was totally embarrassed, not to mention scared.

"Come on, Mary, let's go home," Rosie said.

All the way to home I stared out the back window. I stared into the night, filled with fear and frustration. I had barely gotten into that relationship.

Dear God, it's getting as bad as T. J. and me.

When I arrived home the telephone continued to ring nonstop. Message upon message was left. Eric had definitely lost his mind. Trapped in the wake of that man's madness, I had to find an avenue of escape. I had to disappear before things got totally out of hand. It did not look good—dealing with Eric Richards was overwhelming.

Dr. Jekyll and Mr. Hyde was a monster: a duel personality that changed like the wind. He was far too much for me to handle. It was déjà vu, as I always put me in harms way. I seemed to have a death wish.

That eerie feeling like death had walked over my grave stayed with me. Three days from nowhere, I found myself walking around a gruesome, darkened maze again, trying to find my way out as I tripped over my steps every inch of the way.

Another chapter in my life had turned sour. I still walked that tightrope where it all began in New Jersey. Not to mention there was no safety net to catch me.

What's wrong with me? Am I that desperate to be loved? Will I ever learn?

I needed to take inventory of my life. The reflection I see in the mirror, I did not like or care for.

How many chapters does it take before there's a happy ending? Do I run again? Where does this crazy cycle end? Think, Mary, think. Use your brain for something rather than get into trouble.

In the dark shadows of the night, Eric's presence lurked, even though I did not see him. I felt such ominous, horrible fear. Every sound and quiet beat of my heart—I never knew if or when Eric would surface. I clutched my cold, sweaty hands and wrung them as terror built inside me.

God, I'm scared.

Eric Richards had deep-seated issues and acted out how he felt. He was outraged, out of control, and unraveled at the seams.

That night I anticipated trouble for hours.

This isn't a way to live! I didn't come all this way to be a prisoner in my apartment!

I allowed my crazy, mixed-up emotions to control my life. As soon as another handsome face came along, I was tempted to give into my crazy, unstable emotions. I allowed them to dictate my life. The only person I blamed was me.

I was a grown woman, who—eight years after a bad marriage—should have discerned right and wrong choices. I had become a glutton for punishment, which resulted in me running for my life.

I drove the Manchester Boulevard bus line that entire weekend and worked the graveyard shift. Of all lines to be assigned to, I had been assigned to the one that crossed Main Street, two blocks from where Eric worked. I had a bad feeling—every time I approached that corner street, I anticipated him popping up.

Scared out of my mind, my body became cold and clammy; I did not know how far he would go to make his point. All I knew was Eric was crazy, and I was driving in the middle of the night, not knowing the extent of his craziness.

That entire evening was hell for me. I had not felt such fear since I left Caldwell Hills. As I slowly approached my next stop, I saw Eric in the distance. He wore black trousers and a black knitted sweater. He was decked out in gold and diamonds; he was dressed to kill.

I wanted to pass the stop, but there were too many passengers waiting for the bus. He paid his fare and walked to the back without a sound. For the entire evening, all he did was stare out the back window into the night.

Nothingness ripped through me, and my stomach was upset. My layover was slowly approaching, and I knew he had to get off the bus. I approached the stop slowly, and then looked to see where he was.

Dong! Dong! Dong!

Twelve times I heard that church bell chime. It terrified me and the blackness of the night was mind-boggling. Everything about the darkness brought out the worse in me.

I have a psychopath stalking me! Dear God, what am I going to do?

I kept looking up to watch his every move. I saw him thinking. I sensed his rage from the look on his face, which frightened me.

Dear God, the darkest hour of the night and I'm at the mercy of Eric's madness.

Dong! Dong! Dong!

The sound of the church bell drove me crazy. With cold, sweaty hands, I tried to grip the steering wheel. Eeriness settled in the pit of my stomach and made me wish I was dead.

Why does he just sit there and stare out that window? What's he thinking?

I wanted to shout, scream, or throw him off my bus, but because he was not doing anything, I could not call the transit police. I turned off my engine, and, as I turned around, he was standing directly behind me.

"What do you want, Eric!"

I was in freeze frame and could not move—like I had been paralyzed.

"You lied to me! Do you really think you can just walk out on me?" Eric yelled as he stared down at me.

Trapped between the steering wheel and my seat, I could not move. He had me pinned in—his left arm rested on the back of my seat, his right arm rested on the steering wheel. He crouched over me and laughed with a sinister look on his face.

"What's wrong, Mary? You look terrified. Are you scared of me?"

He laughed and looked crazy. He had a blank stare in his eyes as he grabbed my face and gripped it tightly. I thought he was going to break my jaw.

"Stop, you're hurting me!" I tried to mumble.

My arms were pinned to my side. Trapped between his anger and frustration, I was at the mercy of that madman.

"No one leaves Eric Richards, no one! I'll kill you first, do I make myself clear!" he barked.

The situation seemed helpless. Blackness surrounded me and no one was in sight; I was definitely a sitting duck.

"Mary, why are you doing this? We can be so happy together. I thought you were different!" he shouted. "You haven't seen the last of me. I'll be back."

A flash of light, an oncoming car! God, thank you.

The hushed silence of darkness, piercing sounds of stillness, and anticipation of the ominous thoughts of that man's madness were enough to drive me over the edge. I watched Eric walk away like nothing had happened. He walked down the boulevard and as he turned the corner, I heard the transit police call out to me.

I sobbed and was scared out of my mind. My head pounded and I could not catch my breath. As all sort of emotions ran through me, my mind started to flip through the pages of my life to remind me of what a mess my life had become. I sank into another miry clay pit, my feet were stuck in murky mud, and I grasped on to a shred of hope. I had been between life and death, and the only answer left for me was God.

On my knees in prayer, tears ran down my cheeks. I had stumbled into another entrapment and only God could rescue me from my dreadful nightmare. He always loved me.

I cried with every ounce of life within me until I could cry no more.

Where does my life stop? When does this madness end?

My life had to account for something; my life had to mean something. God does not make mistakes. Once again I stood alone with the Lord by my side.

That crazy cycle seemed to never end. The pages of Eric and me and the long drawn out story with so many curves and changes of events took a toll on my life. I had no idea where to go from I stood. I did not know how to escape my horrific nightmare to which I was chained. It was an unpredictable, uncontrollable chain of events.

Not much was left within me: my sanity rested on a thin sheet of ice. All I had to hold on to was my faith—what little was left. It was the same faith that brought me from New Jersey to California, gave me the courage to board that Trailways bus at Newark Penn Station and sparked a determination to break away from that crazy cycle of T. J. and me. It was the same faith that was predestined to get me through that crazy chapter of my life.

CHAPTER 6

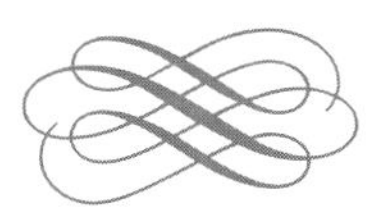

Three Days from Nowhere

My life reflected the many changes that had taken place. In spite of what I had gone through, God was always by my side; I was never alone. Those chapters I had lived built my character and made me the woman God intended me to be.

It was a long race and on many of those days I became weary. My steps skipped and I lost my footing. Regardless, God was always there to pick me up and walk me through.

I was so grateful for my life, even though I had been to hell and back. Those heart-wrenching, horrific chapters I had lived through only seasoned me for the better chapters yet to come.

In California, life had certainly been a challenge; every day was a new experience. Like the chapters before, God was watching over me. He always placed people in my life to either guide me or encourage me. Rosie, Bill, Jane, and Earl were all a part of the many blessings God had bestowed upon me.

Two days before Rosie's birthday, we decided to take her to San Francisco for the weekend. Everything was planned out perfectly. We spent a lot of time down at the waterfront and rode up and down Valencia Street on those gorgeous streetcars, one of San Francisco's historic sights.

The smell of the saltwater was divine and the blue ocean was mild and calm. Even the way the waves hit the shoreline made everything look magnificent. As I looked toward the beautiful sight, I saw whitecap waves blanket the sand, leaving a glistering glow on everything touched.

What I saw captivated me. As I continued to watch the waters of the great Pacific flow freely to and fro, my mind painted a mental picture of God's magnificent creations.

That entire weekend was beautiful. I lost count of the hours we spent under the beautiful sky dome. The nights were breathtaking. I walked in my bare feet along the pier and admired the sights.

"Thank you, guys," Rosie said.

We knew she was happy. Her eyes told the story. As we walked, I heard a familiar voice approach from behind.

"Hello there."

"What?! Arthur Adams! What are you doing here?" I exclaimed with laughter.

"I'm visiting an old buddy," Arthur replied. "So, you finally made it out here! How are the children?"

I momentarily fell silent because I did not know how to respond to his question. However, I knew it was not the time or place to open up to Arthur about my children being taken from me.

"Fine, they're just fine," I replied.

Arthur and I went way back to 1976 when I drove a bus shuttle from Newark International Airport to John F. Kennedy International Airport. He was handsome: 6' 2", dark, curly hair, and had a smile that lit up the world. That man was a sexy, gorgeous marine. Whenever I was with Arthur, I had butterflies in my stomach.

We had become very good friends and, for quite some time, wrote to each other. We managed to see a lot of each other. In fact, he repeatedly asked me to come to California to make a life with him and the kids. I was scared back then and did not have the fight within me.

Many times I wondered if God had brought destiny to me. What I never dreamed was possible became possible. The man of my dreams had found me.

For the remainder of that weekend Arthur and I spent a lot of time together. We had a lot of fun. All sorts of thoughts ran through my mind as my emotions got the best of me.

Am I falling in-love?

I had to come twenty-five hundred miles to be with the man of my dreams. It was a scary thought and I did not want to over-react or assume anything. I did not want to be too impetuous, but I truly wanted to enjoy time with him.

Those three days seemed to pass so quickly. Being with Arthur felt good; I had not really laughed in years. I did not feel threatened or overwhelmed. Arthur made me feel comfortable, I was able to be myself. He was more interested in me and how I felt than he talked about him. We exchanged telephone numbers and planned to see each other again after we each returned to Los Angeles.

For the first time in a long while I was not tense and unnerved. I was so glad to see him. I thought, perhaps, it was a new chapter. Although I knew Eric Richards was alive and kicking, I pushed that thought aside and labeled it: Later.

Monday arrived and I returned to work. I had to work the midnight shift on the Avalon bus line. I drove up and down the boulevard for hours; the bus was packed. Radios blasted, passengers chattered, and in the midst of it all, I had Arthur on my mind. The possibilities of how far our relationship could go intrigued me.

The bus was jammed; there was not one stop where at least fifteen passengers or more did not board the bus. The entire route I thought about the upcoming chapter of my life: *After all these years can destiny be calling out to me? Is this God's hand at work? Am I dreaming?*

What I should have done back then came to me, but because of my stubbornness, it took me more time than it should have. At about ten o'clock that night, the number of passengers on board started to fade. As I approached Florence Boulevard, an all too familiar voice shouted.

"Hello, Mary!"

"What are you doing here, Eric? How did you know my run?"

"You don't seem too happy to see me," he said.

That man stared at me as though he looked through me. He paid his fare and walked to the back of the bus. Once again, he sat in total silence and stared out the window, looking into the blackness of the night. I tried to stay calm and act normal. I could not afford to let on how scared I felt in front of the passengers.

For hours he rode up and down the boulevard, and then sure enough when I reached my layover and the bus was empty, he came to the front.

He shouted and screamed, "You're not getting away with this! You seem to forget who you're messing with you, do you hear me, Mary!"

I stared him down and did not respond to whatever he planned to do. Answering him was not going to change the situation.

"Mary, don't just sit there, answer me!" he repeated. "You're not dumping me . . . Don't make me hit you!"

I did not know how to respond. As scared as I was, there was little I could do at that point.

"I'll be back!" he shouted. "Open the door!"

Eric ran down the bus steps and took off around the corner. I knew I had not seen the last of him. I pulled my bus up to the lamppost so for extra lighting. Since my layover was as long, I did not want to be exposed to pitch darkness in case Eric decided to return.

After about fifteen minutes I turned on the courtesy lamps and took my route sheet out to read it. I sat back in my seat with my legs prompted up on the fare box to await my time to leave. I hated the night shift because it always gave me the willies, especially runs up and down some of those crazy boulevards. I never knew what to expect.

At about 12:01 am, I started the bus engine and slowly turned the corner. I anticipated trouble, but, to my surprise, Eric was not there. At every stop, every layover, I watched for his return and did not let my guard down.

At 2:15 am my run was over and I drove around to the back of the transit division to pull the bus in. I checked my work and walked outside to my car.

Oh no, what's this?

I slowly approached my car and saw a single black rose on its roof. I shivered with fear and my stomach was upset. I perceived someone walked over my grave.

"Eric, what's wrong with you?" I whispered to myself.

I looked around to see if I could spot him. I hurried into my car, started the engine, and rushed out of the parking area. All the way home I stared out the front windshield. I did not know what he was capable of doing. All I knew was he had my attention and that alone scared me.

For days afterwards, I did not hear a thing. It was as though Eric had fallen off the face of the earth. As much as I wanted to believe that was the case, I knew it was the calm before the storm.

All week Arthur called; I was so glad to hear from him. The two of us went to dinner and walked down the pier. It was so nice to sit on the huge rocks, just the two of us. We looked out over the beautiful Pacific. The starry skies were simply heavenly. For the hours we spent out there, the time was simply wonderful.

I was at a loss for words. For a brief moment, my mind drifted back to Mama's attic on Essex Avenue where I was a fairy princess, surrounded by a forty-foot Christmas tree and green ivy that climbed up on the south side of the walls. At thirty-something and twenty-five hundred miles away from New Jersey, I relived that fairytale in the arms of my prince charming.

"It feels good being here with you, angel," Arthur said.

"Me, too. Thanks for being here for me, Arthur."

"You're my special angel. No one will ever hurt you," he said with his beautiful smile.

I sat among the enormous rocks and listened to the sounds of the ocean. As its waves crashed against the shore, I knew I was falling in love again.

"Angel, I love you," Arthur said.

Captivated by the moment, all kinds of beautiful thoughts ran through my mind. A sense of peace overtook me. I released the true feelings of my heart.

"I love you, too, Arthur Adams," I replied.

As I sat there, I embraced the moment; I thanked God for putting Arthur in my life. For every tear I had shed and every sleepless night I had spent, there was a purpose. Those roads travelled were meant to be the pathway to my future. Unknown to me, God was in total control. Once again, because of His love for me, I had transitioned to a new chapter of my life.

While everything happened around me, I still had eerie feelings that gnawed at my heart. I went about my business and took one day at a time. Arthur and I saw each other on a regular basis, and the girls and I still spent time together.

Two weeks before Labor Day, my shift changed. I was truly grateful for the change and did not worry about Eric's sudden appearance. My life had started to look better; things had seemed to mellow out. I was so excited about my new life. Arthur really cared about me and the things I loved. The children were the center of our conversations along with my dreams of getting them back.

Things were running smoothly—too smoothly. It turned out to be the calm before the storm. One Tuesday night when I arrived home from work, I found a bouquet of black roses tied with a black satin ribbon on my doormat. Alongside of them were petals of black roses scattered on my doorsteps. Eric was like a bad dream. I picked up the roses, and as I walked inside the apartment, I saw a dim light flicker on my kitchen table. Its silhouette cast a shadow on my kitchen wall.

"Eric, what are you doing here?" I shouted. "How did you get in?"

He stepped out of the darkness and approached me. He grabbed my arm and muffled my mouth so I was unable to speak.

"Shut up, Mary, or I'll kill you," he whispered quietly in my ear. "We're going for a ride."

We walked down the steps to his car. He opened the door and looked at me.

"Get in," he said.

I was scared and heard my heartbeat. Not a word was spoken; all he did was stare out the front windshield and talked to himself.

"Well, Mary, how do you like your roses," he asked. "Very becoming aren't they?"

I did not know this man and was afraid to say anything. I was too afraid to look at him.

How am I going to get free? Eric's out of his mind.

He drove around for hours. Petrified, I did not know what was to come. Suddenly, he drove into an isolated area with nothing, but huge empty lots with tall, barren trees and tumbleweeds everywhere. He stopped, got out of his car, and walked around to the back to open the trunk.

I was a sitting duck and did not know where we were. I was at the mercy of that madman. He came back to the car. In his right hand he held a long, metal pipe wrench.

"Eric, what are you doing?" I asked. "You're sick and need help! Please Eric, don't do this. I'm sorry, let's try to work things out."

All my senses started to leave when I realized I faced the devil. He took the pipe wrench in his right hand and pushed it up the side of my head. He had an ugly, devilish expression on his face.

"No one leaves Eric Richards!" he shouted. "I thought you were different. Mary, but you're like all the rest. I loved you. God knows I loved you, but you don't love me!"

Time stood still and nothing mattered anymore. Time had already stopped for me.

We sat in his car with the pipe wrench on his dashboard. Eric leaned against the steering wheel and mumbled words I did not understand. Time was running out for me and, even worse, if he killed me, no one would know what happened to me.

I was stuck in a horrific nightmare. I had travelled so far to make a new life only to find I was in the hands of a man, who was unbalanced, twisted, and demented. My heart pounded, and I was so frightened. Every ounce of life seemed to drain from my body. I could not catch my breath; it was like life was slipping away.

Suddenly, a police car appeared and pulled up from the side street by an abandoned building. Eric took notice and quickly grabbed the pipe wrench. He pushed it under his front seat, started the car, and started to drive away.

As soon as Eric reached the first stop sign, I quickly opened the door and got out, hoping I could flag down the officer. When I turned around, the police car was gone. I ran as fast as I could to the Line 81 (Figueroa Street) bus stop and hurried to get on the approaching bus.

Thank God!

Fear washed all over me and I shook like a leaf. As hard as I panted, it was very difficult to catch my breath. All the way home, I stared out the window. When the bus pulled into its layover, I got off and ran home.

That night left me in a fragile state; I could not stay in my apartment any longer. I feared for my life. So, I called Rosie and asked if Bill could pick me up. I stayed at Rosie's and Bill's for quite some time. My mind remained in a state of shock and my emotions ran wild.

Things had to change. My life could not end under those circumstances. If the streets of Los Angeles had not killed me, I was not going to let Eric Richards take my life. My thoughts ran wild, and I feared death; it was all around me.

I had been through so much in my life: I had been burned, beaten, held at gunpoint, pushed down a flight of stairs, and pushed out of a car. Yet, I was still alive and God had a purpose for my life. If my life had not ended before Eric Richards, it was not going to be taken by him either.

CHAPTER 7

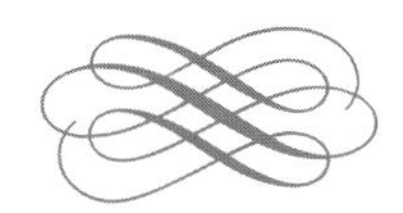

The Walking Dead

My emotions and thoughts had unraveled, which I hated. My feelings were out of control, I thought I had lost my mind. Ever since that night, I lived on an emotional rollercoaster. My life was so complicated, nothing made sense anymore.

Life is not promised, and I had made mistakes. My life meant something to Him, so I was not going to take second best. The life God had given me was to be lived to the full as best I could.

Arthur had picked me up from Rosie's and Bill's place, and I returned home. Upon my return, I grew terrified—the nightmare experience with T. J. flashed before my eyes. I had called the police so many times to no avail because his relationship with personnel within the police department hindered them from taking my cries for help seriously.

"No scars, no bruises, no charges. It's a domestic affair," explained a police officer.

Even when I had injuries to show abuse had occurred, my calls simply made matters worse between me and T. J. I had grown too afraid to call the police any longer because without scars or bruises, I had nothing to show as proof. I feared a repeat of the past. Eric's temperament was like T. J.'s.

What will I do if there's no safety to run to?

As I sat alone on the veranda, the weight of my tears crushed me. Another heart-wrenching chapter of my life had gone badly. The thought of it hurt my heart.

What happened to me? Those dreams, my goals, and the many ambitions I had in life seemed to have evaporated.

There are many stories I wished to write, but those pages lay dormant. Nothing, but blank lines existed. Even the pen on my table awaited its chance to reveal the feelings of my heart.

I still walked around the same mountain, even twenty-five hundred miles from where it all began. At thirty-something I sank, knee-deep, in a pool of bad decisions, wrong choices, and plain stupidity. I was stuck in a cyclone that viciously spun around as I hung on for dear life.

What have I done?

I realized what hinders us from living out our dreams was stubbornness and pride. The two things that cripple us were the very things that caused our dreams die. I prayed for God to save me because He alone could help me. So, I needed to stand on my faith and place my trust in the Lord.

I sat in the veranda for hours in the stillness of the night. My troubled hear was restless, as echoes from the past called out to me. Most of my life had been spent navigating through a concrete jungle. Most years were fought in blood, sweat, and tears. It was only by God's grace that I had kept my sanity.

Eric Richards had truly become my nightmare, a God-forsaken chapter that was tearing me apart. I needed to fight that much harder to get out of that mess.

The quietness of the night gave me an unsettled feeling. I was wrapped up in my mixed emotions as pain tugged at my heart. My entire being was spent: my eyes burned, my head pounded, my heart ached, and I was engulfed in my sorrows. Death was welcomed.

It must have been about 11:00 pm when I heard the church bell chime. Those bells were reminiscent of my school back in New Jersey. Just as the eleventh hour chimed, the telephone rang. I picked up the receiver; it was Eric. He informed me he was coming over. Before I could say another word, he hung up.

Fear and anxiety took a hold of me. I did not want to see him. I cringed at the thought of him coming to my house.

God help me!

I quickly threw on my jacket and ran out the door. I ran so fast I could not catch my breath. I ran down El Segundo Boulevard toward Prairie Avenue; I did not want to confront him. Everything in me was drained; I thought I was going to die as I continued to run.

How does one run from the shadows of death? How can I escape this madness?

As I approached the park, I could not run any further because my legs felt limp. I knew I could not stop there because Eric would see me, so I walked over to the cluster of trees by the lake and hid between the bushes and a rain barrel next to the shed. It was there I spent the night.

That evening was awful. I did all I could to hide far enough from the street so Eric would not find me. As I sat in the midst of darkness, so many scenes flashed before me. Once again, I ran for my life with the same fear I had felt years ago that besieged my mind, body, and soul.

The night sounds stirred and I heard dogs barking from afar. While the sounds of the trains passing through the city sounded close, I also heard their metal wheels slow down on the metal tracks as they blew their whistles. I clutched my knees to my chest and lay my head on them and cried.

I was so far from home in the middle of another terrible nightmare from which I could not wake. That horrendous chapter continued, and I remained in the unbalanced, vicious cycle of Eric and me.

The night grew darker. It had been said midnight is the darkest hour of all. As I sat in the park, crying my heart out, all sorts of crazy thoughts ran through my mind. I wondered if Eric was going to kill me; I was not even halfway through my life. Everything about me was all messed up. Sometimes I dreaded the thought of waking up.

Another horrific chapter of my life had me stuck in the middle chaos. I could not go through life like that anymore. I was petrified and scared out of my mind. That night, I grabbed some change from out of my jacket and caught the bus. I rode up and down Crenshaw Boulevard for the entire night.

Thank God the driver, Larry, knew me. He was unaware of my situation, and I was reluctant to tell him because the outcome was so unpredictable. However, Larry's presence helped me feel safe as I rode the bus.

I wondered when and where Eric would appear. I put nothing past that man. Eric was sick.

Dear God, there's nothing I can do about it.

The entire situation was dreadful. Everywhere I went I looked over my shoulder. That entire night I looked into the darkness of night and wondered if Eric would show up. When I reached 54th Street and Crenshaw Boulevard, I froze. I saw Eric. When I arrived at Liemert Park, Eric's black Camaro was parked across the street from the bus stop by the liquor store.

Oh, dear God, no!

I did not want to get off the bus; I wanted to keep riding. When the bus pulled into the layover, I looked over at the Camaro:

it was empty. I was scared out of my mind. I sat on the bus and did not move; I focused on the Camaro.

Suddenly, it was time to go. As passengers started to board the bus, Eric was among them. My heart pounded and coldness ran through my veins. I felt as cold as a piece of ice. I gasped for air—I thought I was going to die.

I did all I could to avoid eye contact with him, so I focused on the driver. The bus started and slowly drove up to Broadway Street. When it pulled up to the stop, I ran toward the back door and stayed there until I got to the Union Station.

When we arrived there, the bus pulled around to the front of the building. I jumped off and immediately ran toward the light and stayed where people saw me. My heart beat like crazy; there was an eerie and distorted feeling of death that surrounded me. I spun around toward and looked up to where the bus was standing: Eric was gone.

I could not run any further, so I quickly ran to a telephone booth to call Rosie and Bill and asked them to come and get me. As I waited for them, I sat inside the bus depot far away from Eric's madness.

After all that craziness, I was convinced the only thing I could do was to go home, lock myself inside, and hope for a miracle. My fear had crippled me and made me irrational. For their sakes—and a fear of jeopardizing our friendship—I did not want Rosie, Bill, or Arthur involved any deeper.

When I approached the front door of my apartment, there were black roses tied with a black satin ribbon on my front doormat. I was so terrified; I opened the door and rushed inside.

The night seemed to drag on, even the courtyard looked lifeless. It must have been about 4:00 am when I fell asleep on the big, brown leather chair by the bedroom window.

Dong! Dong! Dong!

The church bells chimed according to schedule. Before the fourth hour chimed, the telephone rang.

"Don't ignore me, Mary, call me!" Eric shouted into the message machine.

I unraveled at the seams. For the rest of the night I stayed awake. I did not know what that madman would do. Every car that pulled up to the front of the apartment complex made my heart drop. My life hung in the balance; I did not know how crazy Eric Richards was or if that man would kill me or not.

Stupid me fell right back into that vomit. I could not take the situation much longer; Eric drove me crazy. I was so agitated nothing felt normal—I was wiped out. Whenever the telephone rang, I jumped. So many times I wanted to change that number, but because of the lack of communication between my mother and me, changing the number would make things worse between us.

The dawn of morning started to set in. I saw the sunrise peak through the tall trees at the back of the courtyard.

What a beautiful scene. The glorious colors are brilliantly bright; it illuminates and magnifies the sky.

I was trapped in a frightful nightmare, yet still enjoyed the sunrise. That horrific chapter in my life was more than I bargained for and was far worse than T. J. Masterson had ever put me through. Being so far away from home and familiar surroundings, Like a mouse stuck in a trap, ran on a scroll wheel. I went around in circles as I tried to find my way out.

God knew it would be hard. I struggled to maintain my footing, but no matter how hard I tried, I fell hard like a rock. This time, however, seemed far worse than before.

Days passed, and I heard not a word from Eric. That weekend I wondered what that man was up to. That entire time I worked a late shift. In fact, I worked a double. Instead of my regular run, I worked out of another division.

There was no way for Eric to find me; I was relieved. For most of that Saturday evening, I worked the freeway flyer, and then I jumped over to the Hermosa Beach run. I worked until 2:30 am and was famished. So, on the way home I decided to stop at the all-night diner to pick up a chocolate shake.

It was a spring-like evening. The stars were out and the sky was simply lovely. I even heard birds chirp in the fullness of the trees surrounding the mall. I picked up my shake and walked alongside the mall's parking lot to take a shortcut home.

As I walked and drank my shake, I remained aware of my surroundings.

What a lovely night.

Even a cute, little Calico cat walked alongside me. I fed him a few pieces of crackers I found in my pocket. The two of us had a lovely conversation as we made our way through the mall. Suddenly, I heard something very strange. The quietness had been interrupted by the rustling of leaves behind me.

I quickly looked around, but saw nothing. Yet, the sounds grew louder, so I started to walk faster toward the apartment complex. My heart was throbbing, and I broke into a cold sweat. I walked as fast as possible with my little friend beside me.

Suddenly, the black Camaro swung directly in front of me. I tried to jump out of its path, but every time I moved, the car moved with me.

"Get in the car, Mary!" Eric shouted as the passenger door swung open.

I turned quickly and ran in the opposite direction. I weaved in and out of the parking structure and around the big, stone pillars to get away from him. There was nothing, but complete silence. All I heard was the echo of my shoes running along the concrete slabs.

I ran fast and tried to get away from him. I ran so hard I gasped for air. Suddenly, Eric came from behind and grabbed my arms. He muffled my mouth and dragged me to his car. He threw me in and drove for miles. Then, he got on the 91 Freeway and kept driving.

The radio blasted as Eric sat there pounding the steering wheel with his fist. He sang to that heavy metal music, which sent chills up and down my spine. The look on his face was simply horrible. He was so angry and talked to himself. Then, he drove off an exit and turned into a remote, desolate area and stopped.

"Eric, please," I pleaded.

"Shut up!" he snarled.

The look on his face was scary. He was so angry he pushed the seat back, grabbed me, pulled me down, and raped me. I tried to scream, but his hand was tightly around my mouth. I was pinned down and could not move. He went crazy as sweat poured down his face and dripped into my eyes. Fear suffocated me.

God, he's hurting me.

I came apart at the seams; nothing felt right. As I flipped through the pages of my mind, I saw the same scene repeated. Ugly memories of Uncle Jerry and me, and the many nights I was caught up in his demented world. Once again, I was in way over my head. Troubled waters surround me as I drowned in another pool of filth.

Where I would go from there was a big question for which I had no answer. Using my own strength, I knew I could not fight the devil, Eric Richards. Scrambled thoughts raced through my mind, and I tried to unravel them. It was a bitter pill to swallow, which tore at me. After chapters of love lost between my mother and me, I had searched for love in all the wrong places. As a result, I had a thorn in my side.

That night was a living hell. Eric had unleashed his anger and hatred, and had taken all his vengeance out on me. His hand was so tight around my throat I could hardly breathe. Suddenly, I felt faint and believed I was going to pass out.

That night was as horrible as the nights in the early 1950s—those horrible years of Uncle Jerry and me. Even then I wished I was dead. Every moment seemed a lifetime that lasted forever. I relived that same nightmare.

When it was over, Eric pulled me out of the car and left me there with torn clothes. My body ached and head pounded. I had been violated and betrayed. I walked over to and sat under one of the huge trees. I leaned against the trunk and sobbed.

It was pitch black out there. I pulled myself up and fumbled through the dark to find my way out of there. Everything about me was crushed under the shame and pain of what had just happened.

Suddenly, I saw blurred lights ahead. It was the freeway. I walked as quickly as I could, and when I approached it, a lady in a dark blue van stopped to help me. I was so grateful to see a friendly face. As tears ran down my face, I thanked her for being kind to me.

I hurt so badly I could not say another word. I just sat in total silence and looked out the window while the rest of me drifted away. Everything about me was spent, I was numb, even my mind stopped thinking. My entire body was crushed and my emotions ran cold and dry. Despite all the tears I had shed, my face felt dry. My eyes burned and my thoughts were void.

Eric Richards had dragged me into his demented world. Somehow, I became his threshing post and every bit of his twisted emotions had been taken out on me. He beat me down with the feelings of his heart. I shut down and truly felt nothing. All that remained in me was emptiness and fear. A cold, eerie feeling ran through my body; I was slipping away.

Ever since that night I lived on the edge. I stayed to myself and was so beside myself I had no words to say to anyone. My mind was in another world, far from reality.

I had drifted into a world all too familiar that reached back to the days in Mama's attic. Way back to the early 1950s when I ran to get away from Mama and Uncle Jerry to a place where I could find shelter and pray for someone to rescue me.

CHAPTER 8

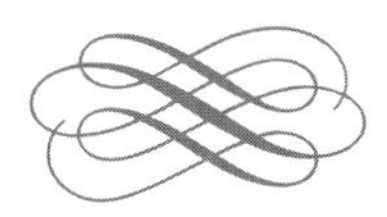

Extreme Fear

Most of the chapters of my life had been complicated and disappointing. I was once again in a chapter far from being over and so uncertain. I was extremely fearful, and without a doubt, left no room for error. Since that night I had made a lot of decisions. I knew I could not stay where I was because Eric would kill me.

After much thought, I decided to take a leave of absence from my job and headed up North. I took what I had saved and made plans to disappear for a while. I hoped and prayed that, perhaps, Eric would fall off the face of the earth.

I had lived in and out of suitcases most of my life. It seemed as though I could not get anything right. At thirty-something I still travelled around that same mountain.

That week I took care of business and went down to the division. Then, I told Rosie and Bill I was going away for a while and would return after things had cooled down. I truly did not know if anything would get better. As for Arthur, I did not know what to say to him, which truly broke my heart.

I started to pack my things, and that Friday night I left to go up North. My heart was very troubled as I pulled up roots to leave. Once again I had put me in a precarious situation. I was scared. I never gave my apartment manager notice I had planned to leave; I just up and left.

I boarded a Greyhound bus on 7th Street—history repeated itself. As the bus pulled out of the station, tears filled my eyes and rolled down my cheeks. I remembered another time when I had been forced to leave my little world behind: the night I left New Jersey.

I arrived in Sunnyvale, an old stomping ground where T. J. and I had gotten married in 1965. I rented a small studio apartment and purchased a 1979 Chevy Mazda. I got a job as a waitress and barmaid at the Golden Spur, a diner by the town square.

I did not know how long it would take me to return to Los Angeles, so I made the best of it. Confused and beside myself, there was not a day when I did not shed a tear. Heartbroken, I still prayed for a miracle and trusted in God for my life. My days were long, but those lonely heartfelt nights took a lot out of me. I cried myself to sleep and waited for someone to rescue me.

My heart still ached at thirty-something. Alone and scared, I had to once again hide to survive. Discouraged and very depressed, I had totally disconnected from everyone; I did not even write to Rosie and Bill. My emotions ran wild and I experienced so many mood swings, it drove me crazy.

I was so angry with me I could have set the world on fire. My mind kept messing with me and I was unsure of myself. Life had drained and crushed me under the weight of the problems I bore. There were times when I surmised I was trapped underneath what had come down on me.

I continued to work night after night. I drowned in my sorrows while I drank white Chamblaise and cried. There were a lot of changes to which I had to adapt. The chapters of my life continued and the pages kept turning as the stories continued to be written. The pen stroked out the feelings of my heart.

I wished I could go return to happier seasons of my life, but I knew I could not. Those chapters were embedded in the far corners of my mind; a place where memories lay, only to be remembered occasionally.

I had not adjusted well to my new lifestyle; everything was up in the air. I continued to call back home. Although things were not changing, I kept trying. I hoped and prayed one day I could get through to my family. Maybe one day we can move on and be a family again.

I was stuck inside a chapter I did not want to be. I had come all the way North to get away from that madman and sat in the darkness of night, trying to figure out how I got caught up in another bad situation. Stuck between a rock and a hard place, I tried to gather the shattered fragments of my life, piece them together, and make sense of the life I had lived.

I grabbed onto the only remnants left: dreams deferred, pieces scattered before me, fragments of the life I had lived, which had meant so much to me. Faded by time, all that remained were memories. I closed my eyes and envisioned soaring through the sky on the wings of an eagle over the mountain and through the clouds. I planned to keep flying on until victory cries out.

As I sat under the beautiful sky, the presence of my Lord surrounded me. I was lost in the peace of God and awaited the Lord to rescue me. In spite feelings I had, I knew I had a lifetime of work ahead of me. I wanted to start writing again, so I jotted down my accomplishments in my journal.

I wanted to move forward. I did not want to stand still—my life means more than that. If I remained stagnant, I was going to be trapped in my terrible nightmare. Whatever I had dreamed of was to be lost forever in that vicious cycle.

Where had life gone wrong, Lord, What have I done to end up like this?

I could not seem to shed the ugly feelings and emptiness that ate at my heart. It was killing me. I hurt so bad I wanted to die. I gathered my memories one-by-one and wrapped them around me, embraced the pain, cried out, and hoped God heard me.

I had run twenty-five hundred miles to make a new life, and did not know if I would ever get it right. In the midst of my tears, I picked up my pen and began to write the continuation of my life's story. I was so drained; much of me was spent, but I had to keep believing one day my life would turn around to the good. Somewhere, I would have a happily-ever-after ending.

I sat among the gorgeous flowers in the middle of the courtyard, over by the gorgeous waterfall, to write. The waterfall—what a magnificent piece of white stone pillars with angels surrounding them, and water cascades rushing down the enormous pillars and splashing into a pool of lights.

I sat for hours as I bore my soul. I wrote tear-jerking stories about my life. As my tears fell onto the pages, the lettering of the words was smeared, and like the fading of time, the words were gone forever. Only memories remained.

I went to work that night and saw Paulie, one of Eric's drummers. He sat at the back table and watched me. I stayed at the tables at the back of the diner until Paulie left. I was puzzled about why he was there. I was miles away from Los Angeles, yet part of my nightmare still followed me.

This is so crazy . . . Paulie will surely tell Eric where I am! No matter where I go, Eric finds me!

I was paranoid because I knew if he found me, he would kill me. Every noise I heard, even the crackling sound that came from the floorboard in my apartment made me jump. I could not live like that. My mind worked overtime. I perceived I sat on the outside looking into one of the darkest hours of my life.

My mind took me back to the early 1950s as I curled up under Daddy's workbench locked in the furnace room. I sobbed, as I still felt the cold concrete and smelled the stench of the cellar walls. I was locked in that cold, dark room surrounded by the roar of the flames that came from the chamber doors of that big, old red furnace.

"Mommy, Mommy! Please don't leave me; I'm scared," I cried.

A little child, no more than six years old, was scared out of her mind. I listened to those flames roar as they burned in the walls of that big, metal furnace.

"Stupid little girl! Why did I have you? Why God gave me you instead of my boys, I'll never know!" she shouted.

God, why am I reminiscing about this? Lord, I'm losing my mind.

I saw me on that basement floor as I rocked back and forth with my knees close to my chest with my arms clasped around them. I heard those flames and saw those bellows move.

That sound, that hideous sound from that furnace!

I still tried to figure out why Mama did not love me. After all this time, I should have let go, but the question haunted me. I was chained to that season of my life, so I drown in tears and prayed to God to help me.

Staying in Sunnyvale was not working. I was so unfamiliar with my surroundings. Somehow, someway I had to get back to Los Angeles. I had to stop running because no matter how hard I ran, life always seemed to find me. Unless I fought back, I would lose.

Enough was enough. I could not go through life in full sprint any longer. I had to stop and not allow the child within me to continue running. I was a grown woman with a life to live, so I had to take charge.

I was not even halfway through this life, yet that rollercoaster seemed never ending. I was self-destructing and if I did not stop, I was going to go over the edge. I could not let the devil win and refused to throw in the towel.

The seasons, which have come and gone, had a great impact not only on my life, but also the lives of my family members. Many chapters took me by storm and had been hard ones to live through. It was only by the grace of God I survived to talk about it.

From Essex Avenue to California, and everything in between, those chapters detailed the life I had lived, and the character life had built. God had been so good to me. He walked me through each storm and whenever was drowning, the Lord picked me up, carried me, and continued alongside me on my journey.

In Sunnyvale, I had met some good people, who really cared for me. God always put special people in my life to either comfort or encourage me. Throughout the many seasons of hardship, from the shattering nights of the 1950s to episodes T. J. and I experienced through the grueling chapters of Uncle Jerry and me, God had always been there for me. He picked me up and extended His grace, using the people in my life as His hands and feet.

It had been God's way of showing He loved me. Those very people represented God's work of love. I thanked the Lord every day for those beautiful souls.

There were no words to describe the true feelings of my heart. I was as lost as I could be. Ahead I saw a fork in the road that bore to the right and left. My life had been one disaster after another. So, truly frightened, I was unsure about which way to go.

All of my life I had believed in God. Even as a child I got on my knees by my bedside and cried out to ask God for miracles. I still prayed for God to answer me twenty-five hundred miles away from where it all began.

As each season passed I would not give up hope because that same God, who had delivered me once, would deliver me again. I waited with expectancy and rested in His love.

Ten hours and six hundred miles away, I still wrestled with Eric Richards syndrome. Many nights I lay awake and pictured a beautiful watercolor painting of my life. My dreams, goals, aspirations, my entire life was brilliantly designed in the colors of a rainbow. Yet, I was surrounded by the craziness of Eric and me. So much within me had to be put on hold.

I tried so hard to work through the piles of nothingness, but that vicious cycle slowed me down. I worked that much harder to rid me of his crazy nonsense and tried to stay positive.

However, since Paulie had seen me, I was unsure. Everything seemed like I was stuck in quicksand—with every step I sank deeper into a bottomless pit. I planned each day carefully to avoid Paulie Henderson. I did not trust him and kept in mind he was one of Eric's best friends.

I never knew from one day to the next what lurked around the bend. Questions, some of which have no answers, swirled in my mind about what my tomorrows may bring, when Eric Richards would strike again. I tried to keep my footing to stay on track.

Life was like climbing a mountain: up hill all the way with jagged pieces of rocks, tiny stones that cut, and an overwhelming steepness. My mountains, like life's trials, had knocked the wind out of me. My life had been one extraordinary climb, a remarkable journey that kept me on my toes. Yet, I had not reached the summit.

From where I stood, that enormous mountain looked like a huge monster. I was tired; there were times I wanted to give up, throw in the towel, and quit.

How much can one person take?

Thoughts like that scared me and rattled my mind. Thank God I had determination. Although my journey had been a long one, I had made up my mind a very long time ago that come hell or high water I was not quitting. That chapter of Eric and me had taken a major toll on me, it kicked me hard; yet, I stayed in prayer. God was the only One who could help me.

Days seemed to last forever and my mental state had been worn down. I felt lost and broken-hearted. I had taken a big chance leaving my world behind, burning bridges, and cutting the lines of communication. I stood between a rock and a hard place, and did not know if that move had been directed by God.

The only thing that kept me afloat was my faith and knowing God does not make mistakes. I was sure God would have stopped me before I continued. I had travelled far and worked hard. I had endured much. Common sense told me that was not the time to quit.

Life was hard, but very rewarding. I had heard it said anything worth having is worth fighting for. Like in a big box of chocolates, I never knew what I would get from life until I bit into it. I truly appreciated where I was, for it had taken a lot of blood, sweat, and tears to arrive there. When I looked back through the corridors of my mind, I reflected on how far I had come by the grace of God.

Where I would go from that chapter being written was another question. It had been said the harder the climb, the greater the victory. Thank God I had managed to get through life with as little battle scars as possible. No matter how close to the edge I had come, God always pulled me back; I never went over.

At thirty-something I still climbed my mountain. I had not given up. Whenever those negative thoughts played heavily in my mind I cast them out, shook them off and I kept pushing and pressing forward. It was my life, and since I had just one life to live, it was how I lived that would determine if I would win.

One day I hoped to get it right; however, when? I truly did not know how many more chapters needed to be written. That, too, was questionable. God had given me life, and I could not allow anyone or anything to rob me of what the Lord had given me. It was up to me to make or break it.

I had choices: quit or keep fighting. A fighter at heart, I did not know how to quit. I was an overcomer, an achiever. If T. J. Masterson did not win, Eric Richards would not win either.

Like a bird locked in a cage, once the doors opened there was no stopping the bird's flight. Scary as that chapter may have been, I needed to move on. With tear-filled eyes, and a very confused mind, I stood on my faith and believed in my heart God would see me through that chapter in my life.

CHAPTER 9

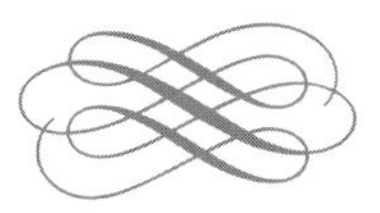

The Night Stalker

Out in left field, I tried to get my bearings; I had lost my footing. Unsure of everything since that incident at the club, I was more scared than ever.

After great thought, I started to write Rosie and Bill. I did not want them to think I had forgotten them. I wrote a long letter to explain the things that had happened in Sunnyvale. Afterwards, I wrote a letter to Arthur to give him my telephone number and address. I never dreamed how bad things had gotten and it definitely had to end. I was tired of running; the wind in my sails had finally stopped.

Running in circles drove me crazy. Day after day I looked over my shoulder; I feared Eric would find me. How sad it was to not only deal with that man's madness, but to also face Eric's friend, Paulie. Night after night, in the early hours of the morning, I would be scared as I came home from work. My fear crippled and hindered me from living a normal life.

I never dreamed I would be stuck in such madness, drowning in a pool of fear and confusion. I tried to figure out how I got involved in that entire situation; I did not see it coming. Eric had me fooled. Life was too precious and I had lost out on much of my life running in and out of the shadows and from insanity.

I remained on the run and trapped in a vicious web. My life consisted of work and returning home. I was too afraid to indulge in anything else, as my mind played games and I saw things that were not there. Yet, I knew someone lurked in the shadows of the night; I sensed the person's presence.

Days seemed like weeks, weeks seemed to last forever. My nerves were knotted like a ball of yarn. I had to do something as a means of release, so one Saturday evening I took a ride to Market Street and walked around the square for a while.

It was good to get out. I needed a breath of fresh air, but as I sat on the bench near the ice cream parlor, I saw Paulie. He was talking to someone. I started to walk over to him, but I lost sight of him.

Where did he go?

"Paulie, Paulie!" I shouted.

God I'm losing my mind! Where is he?

Once again fear took hold of me. I ran up Market Street and caught the Number 16 bus route back home. During the ride I looked out the side window and waited for Paulie to pop up.

It was so dark that night; the only thing that pierced through the darkness was the redundant sound of jets flying overhead. I looked up and did not see a thing, yet the sound was seemingly right above me.

When I arrived at the stop near by home, I got off the bus and took a shortcut through the park. I walked as fast as I could. As I approached the lake, I saw Pauli's red Mustang parked by the big willow tree near an abandoned toolshed.

No, I've got to get out of here! What's he doing here?

My legs felt like they weighed a hundred pounds. I could not move fast enough. Fear took hold of me, as he sat in his car with his high beams on. My fear was so overwhelming, it crippled me. I fell to my knees in horror.

At that point I did not care any longer. I had nowhere to run or hide. If my life had to end at that moment, then so be it. I could go no further.

"Mary, I'm not here to hurt you. Let me help you, please," Paulie said.

I was so terrified I could not move.

"Mary, please let me help you," he repeated.

He walked in front of me and extended his hand. I sobbed so hard, even my hands trembled.

"Mary, Eric's looking for you. He found out where you work, so please let me help you," he urged.

We must have remained at the park for hours as we sat under the big pine trees and talked about Eric.

"Mary, our band plays up here quite often. He has a lot of friends here, too," Paulie explained.

I was so confused and beside myself. No matter how hard I tried to escape that man, I could not.

"Paulie, where do I go from here?" I asked. "I have nowhere else to go."

I held my knees to my chest and clasped my arms around them. My hands were gripped tightly together as I sobbed. I was on the run again, but this time I was running out of time. My body was tired and exhausted; my head pounded so badly I found it hard to think. All that I had left was my will to survive.

"Paulie, is Eric here?" I asked.

"No, Mary, but he's on his way," he replied.

Paulie drove me back to the club. I packed my things and stopped to speak to Sam. It broke my heart because Sam had become a good friend. He had done so much for me, but I had to tell him I was leaving. Once again, I fell into another trap far worse than T. J. Masterson's grasp.

Make no mistake; I blamed me for all of that drama. I should have been a better judge of character. Wrong. When I thought I had moved forward I fell flat right on my face—shame on me. There was no time to feel sorry for myself; I could not afford a pity party. I had to get back up and make it happen. After leaving the Golden Spur, Paulie drove me back home. I was so frightened I froze at my front door.

"Paulie, this isn't a trap, right? Eric isn't in there waiting for me, is he?" I asked.

"Mary, go inside, Eric isn't here. I wouldn't do that to you," he replied.

I cautiously put the key in the lock and slowly turned it. I walked inside. It was so dark. All I saw was the kitchen light on over the stove. I felt so uncomfortable and edgy. My whole body was tense.

God, I'm falling apart.

That whole situation was incredible; it was a complete nightmare. Eric Richards had become a thorn in my side. He tried so hard to make me believe he was something when he was not. In the beginning there were no signs. He had a striking, distinctive character and a strong personality. He appeared to be a man who had it all.

After nine months, I had met another Dr. Jekyll and Mr. Hyde. How morbid it was to deal with someone who was not in his right mind that changed like the wind. Eric was a man of many personalities. I was not prepared to deal with that issue.

"Paulie, where do I go from here?" I asked.

"Mary, you can't stay here. Eric will find you," he replied.

I did not know who to trust. Although it seemed like Paulie cared, he was Eric's friend, so I did not trust him either. After he left, I had a lot of thinking to do. I drew my curtains and lit a candle on the table by the window. I sat down and wrote letters to Rosie, Bill, and Arthur.

As tears fell and my hands shook. I found it difficult to hold the pen steady. Every tear that falls on the paper smudged what I had written.

My heart raced as I wrote each line. The brokenness inside gushed out of me as I expressed the emotions of my heart. For hours I sat and watched the candle's wick burn down as the wax melted.

Tuckered out, I sat with my thoughts. When I looked outside my window, I saw the first sign of dawn break through the trees and peek through my venetian blinds. I got up, took a shower, I walked to the mailbox to mail the letters. My mind was consumed with how that chapter would end.

My life had become so complex. Like a patchwork quilt, the threads and seasons of my life were so intricately sown. Sometimes, the interwoven patterns made things very difficult and hard for me.

Eric was pernicious, angry, malicious, and acted wickedly. The time we had spent together caused much hardship and tears. I did not know how to get rid of that man; walking away from him was not the answer. Eric Richards did not easily let go; he was a control freak. The harder I tried, the worse my situation became.

I did not know where things had begun. I did not know where that road would end. The nightmare seemed never ending. I had to concentrate on my next steps and had to avoid Eric. I simply could not allow him to find me.

That weekend Rosie and Bill called, as did Arthur. It was so nice to hear their voices. Within days, Rosie and Bill came up. Shortly thereafter, Arthur arrived, too. It felt so good to see familiar faces. I did not feel alone anymore. Together, the four of us worked things out. Arthur insisted I stay with him; he was not afraid of Eric. Rosie and Bill made arrangements to drive me back to Los Angeles.

I was so grateful for what they were doing for me. Someone truly loved me; that, alone, blessed my heart. Two days before they left, I stopped at St. Mary's Church to light a few candles. I knelt down to pray and thanked God for another miracle.

While I was there, those gorgeous, huge, brass metal bells chimed: Dong! Dong! Dong! How I loved the sound of bells. That sound took me way back to the early 1950s when Daddy, Mommy, and I walked up the hill to Chapel Street to visit Grandma Jilliano's grave.

What a beautiful day that was. The sun shone so brightly, and the sky was a beautiful powder blue. As I looked up toward the heavens, I saw the white, puffy, dome-shaped cumulus clouds scattered across the sky.

I walked down to the little park next to the cemetery and admired the day; there was such a beautiful peace. As I sat there, I rested; my mind cleared and I experienced such joy and comfort. It seemed as though God's arms had wrapped around me to reassure me everything was going to be all right.

Hours must have passed. Arthur came down the street. I waved to and smiled at him. I was not afraid anymore.

Eric can't hurt me.

I got up and met Arthur halfway. When we met, he took me in his arms and hugged me for a brief moment. I felt alive again. Arthur reassured me everything was going to be all right; no one was going to hurt me or make me cry. I had a personal angel.

God still sends people my way to encourage and strengthen me. I am truly grateful and can never repay the Lord for all He has done for me. All I can do is live my life so God will be pleased with me.

After a few days in Sunnyvale, Arthur had to go up to Palo Alto to see his grandmother. From there, he had planned to go back to Los Angeles. Rosie and Bill started to make arrangements for us to travel back to their place. Since I had my car, Bill had to get a truck with a hitch to take all my things with us.

I had enough of Sunnyvale and was ready to leave. Bill had to make a stop first at San Francisco, so I was not able to go with them because they had two or three days more on the road. I was mentally drained; it hurt too much to think. My life had spun out of control for so long that I was a bundle of nerves.

Eric had done all he could to terrorize me. One thing I had on my side was my faith, which gave me determination to build a strong will to survive.

Halfway through the week I kept busy packing. I could not wait to leave. As busy as I was, I tried to call back home to speak to my mother. The telephone rang repeatedly; it rang at least thirty times or more, but nobody answered. I continued to try to get through until that evening, hoping my mother would pick up. Unfortunately, no matter how hard I tried I could not get through.

After about an hour or so I gave up and continued to pack. Halfway through packing, something very strange happened. Just outside of my apartment, there was a lot of commotion. I heard people taking down in the courtyard. I looked through my front window and saw two policemen standing by the fountain searching for something or someone with their flashlights. Suddenly, the telephone rang.

"Hello," I said.

No one answered. There was complete silence on the other end.

"Hello, is there somebody there?" I asked. "Hello, who is this?"

Click.

The telephone was hung up. Like a gust of wind, an outburst of emotion went through me. Every part of me fell apart. That sudden fear struck me again, and I grew colder. My entire body felt as cold as ice. The telephone kept ringing, but I was too frightened to pick it up. My fear paralyzed me. I could not get my thoughts straight.

Once again, everything inside me went wild. I was sick to my stomach. Nothing, but twisted, distorted visions of that crazy man flashed through my mind and terrorized me.

Dong! Dong! Dong!

The church bells.

The sky was dark outside, and I saw storm clouds form. It turned out to be an ominous, scary night. Thunder clapped, lightning flashed, and somewhere out there the boogey man stalked me.

I sat by the fireplace and watched the sky light up. I pulled my knees close to my chest and heard my heart pound as the flood-gates of heaven opened. The rain poured. A memory opened up to me as I watched the rain fall. I remembered Mama's attic back on Essex Avenue and the endless hours Sporty, Miss Molly, and I watched the rain fall.

We snuggled up underneath the rafters of the pitch roof, covered by one of Mama's old wooly blankets. I got drowsy and sleepy-eyed as I watched the rain fall.

There were many endless, beautiful, glorious nights the three of us spent in that attic, cuddled together. We watched the heavy rain hit the sides of the house and heard it pound on Mama's roof. The raindrops swirled around in circles in the puddle they made. Something about the rain was so peaceful to me. Even as a child, I wrapped me in one of Mama's old wooly blankets and allowed the sound of the rain to lull me to sleep.

However, that night was much different; I felt threatened. The darkness of the night scared me and as the rain pounded against the windowpane, I kept seeing Eric's face pierce though the shadows of the night.

It was getting late and the apartment had become quite chilly. So, I put a piece of firewood in the fireplace and grabbed the blue floral quilt from off the closet shelf. I wrapped it around me and fell asleep.

Suddenly, I was awakened by a loud thump. I quickly got up and looked around. As I approached the kitchen, I saw blaring lights through the kitchen window. I slowly walked over to the window and gently opened the blinds. I peeked out and saw a strange car idle in front of the apartment complex.

I looked intensely, but no one got out. After a few moments or so, the engine stopped. I could not see who sat inside.

It's him! I know it's him!

He tormented me.

Why doesn't he just get out of the car and get it over with?

I backed away from the window and grabbed the telephone. I started to dial the police, but stopped when I heard a faint knock on the door.

Is it my door? Oh, God, it's him! I know it's him! I fretted as I dropped the telephone.

I quickly picked up the telephone and tried to dial the police again. Before I finished dialing, I heard footsteps outside my door. My hands trembled; I could not breathe. My stomach was in knots.

As hard as I tried to dial the number, I kept messing up. My legs and head felt funny. I thought I was going to pass out. Life seemed to drain from my body and I was spent. I stared at the door as scenes of my life flashed before me.

Once again, I was alone; stuck between the chapters of my life. I held on to a shred of hope that something would get me through that night. My fears crippled me and my thoughts were disarranged. I could not function; everything about me seemed so disheveled.

God, I can't hide in here forever. This crazy fear has taken over my mind, body, and soul. If I don't stop now, God, I'll be paralyzed forever.

CHAPTER 10

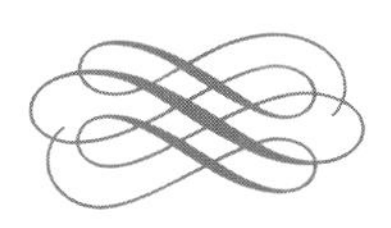

Wrong Turn

I thought I was going to die. I could not wait any longer and wanted to leave right away. I tried to call Arthur, but he did not answer. Since his grandmother did not have an answering machine, I had difficulty reaching him. I tried for hours. Even Rosie and Bill were hard to reach.

It was getting very late and I could not wait any longer. So, I threw the rest of my things into suitcases. As I headed out the door, the telephone rang.

"Hello, hello," I said.

Click.

The telephone continued to ring.

"Hello, hello . . . Answer me!" I yelled.

There was absolutely nothing said on the other end. All I heard was a dead silence and hideous, heavy breathing.

"Hello, hello!" I repeated.

"Well, Mary, I'm here," Eric said smugly with a hideous laugh.

I got so scared I dropped the receiver. My body shook as I sobbed. I could not catch my breath and anticipated dying.

"Mary, I'm coming over!" he shouted.

This is ludicrous!

I realized I had not grabbed my keys when I initially ran to the front door in a panic. So, I snatched them off my bed, bolted out the door, and ran down the steps through the courtyard. I did not look back. I ran to the carport, threw my things into the car, and left. I was terrified and emotionally out of it; I was losing my mind.

Tears filled my eyes and had a burning sensation. Everything was a big blur. I drove down the back streets because I did not want Eric to see me. I drove fast and hard. As I ran for my life, I remained mindful of the signs to the freeway.

Scared, confused, and emotionally distraught, I was falling apart.

I prayed, "God, help me, please! Don't let Eric find me!"

I kept driving and suddenly, I saw the freeway sign.

"The freeway, thank God!" I shrieked.

I made a left turn and got onto the freeway. That was a dark, cold night; the blackness of the night seemed so threatening and made my skin crawl. Suddenly, through all that darkness, bolts of lightning flashed across the sky, some blinding. Thunder rolled, winds blew, and the darkness made everything creepy—I was scared out of my mind.

"Dear God, where am I?" I cried out.

Frustrated and out of sorts. I actually freaked out. Never did I travel on the freeway before, let alone at night. When I came to Sunnyvale, it was by bus, so I was totally turned around.

I had no telephone, no way to reach anyone. That was enough to blow my mind. The entire night all I saw was blaring lights from oncoming traffic, and bright red vehicle brake lights in front of me.

The rain came down in buckets and was so heavy it made it difficult to see the road ahead. Although, the windshield wipers did their best, visibility was at almost zero.

That was a night I would never forget. My heart was troubled, my mind hurt, and nothing, but negativity ran through my veins.

That night was wet, cold, and frightening. The only contact I had with reality was the rain, thunder, and lightning.

I rode in pitch blackness. The night looked the way I felt. Nothing, but nothingness was around as I drove. I looked at my gas gauge: it read a quarter of a tank.

I prayed, "Lord, I'm going crazy. The silence is driving me up a wall."

The freeway seemed endless, and as the rain fell heavily onto my car, I wondered what would happen if Eric found me. I did not know where I was and the road signs were foreign to me. My eyes became heavy. I was so exhausted and too afraid to blink. I did not want to fall asleep behind the wheel. In the middle of my numbness, I pulled over to the shoulder of the road and rested for a while.

My eyes burned and were puffed up from crying. I decided to close them a bit. Suddenly, I was awakened by something that startled me. I looked around, but there was absolutely nothing; I was imagining things. I regrouped and realized the rain had not let up, so I continued to drive.

The weather was bad and the temperature grew colder; I started to shiver. When I left my house, I only had on a sweater. I looked at my watch, which had stopped: it read midnight. My radio did not work, so I was lost time-wise. I saw a detour sign ahead, which read: Freeway Closed. I followed the sign and got off the exit.

When I got to the end of the road, I made a left turn. I was truly lost and kept looking for another entrance back onto the freeway. I saw nothing but huge trees, telephone poles, and abandoned lots. The temperature had gotten colder, and I shook like a leaf. The rain came down in buckets, and thunder and lightning were everywhere. In fact, the only light for miles was lightning strikes ahead.

"God, I'm lost, I'm truly lost. Where am I? How did I get into this mess? How stupid can I be?" I asked myself.

Finally, I saw a sign ahead that read: Gas, Food, and Lodging 2 miles. It was so difficult to see the road and I did not want to miss the turn-off. So, I slowed my speed until I got there.

"God it's deserted! What happened?" I said aloud.

I pulled up to the station and blew the horn, but no one was there. After a few moments or so, I got out of the car and walked to the office. The sign on the door read: Close for Repairs.

I walked to the telephone booth next to the restroom and tried to call Rosie and Bill again, but the line was busy. The rain came down so hard I was drenched. The rain was so cold my feet numbed.

I tried to call them again, but the line remained busy. I could not wait any longer, so I ran back to my car. As I opened the door, I saw a silver truck parked on the side of the road. It faced me. I froze. As the rain came down, I shivered and stared at the lights in front of me. Someone was in that truck—a man with dark glasses.

Dear God, it must be him! I know it's Eric!

I quickly got into my car. As I started the engine, the pickup truck pulled up directly behind me. I was so nervous, my body shook. I gasped for air. When I made a left turn at the end of the road, the silver truck followed behind me. My stomach was in knots as if my insides were coming out.

Those blaring bright lights and high beams were directly on me. I could not see because the lights blinded me. I tried to shield my eyes from the lights to mitigate the glare to no avail.

That long, winding, stretch of road was unbelievable. It was like something out of a horror movie. The road became slicker, and my wheels started to spin. I slowed my speed to avoid running off the road. I looked in my rearview mirror and saw those blaring lights; that truck was right on top of me.

"Oh, God, help me! I'm going to die!" I cried out.

I knew I had to compose myself, as my heart raced; my whole body shook uncontrollably. As cold as it was, I was sweating. There was no one else on the road, except that hideous pickup and me.

The gas gauge on my car read low, and there was not a gas station in sight. I tried to focus on the white lines in the road, but the poor visibility made my eyes heavy and itchy. The road was so slick my tires slid. The windshield wipers did their best, but the rain came down so hard, it continued to impair my vision.

The lights of the pickup blinded my eyes, and I suddenly slammed on my brakes because thought something had run in front of my car. I went into a total tailspin, which turned the car around 180 degrees. When I looked up the silver pickup truck faced me with its light shone directly on me.

I experienced a combination of fear and frustration; I could not take it anymore. The car continued its tailspin and came to a halt before I went over the embankment. I was so beside myself I got out of the car and screamed.

"Eric, is that you?" I yelled. "Whatever you're going to do, just do it!"

The rain came down in buckets, and tears fell from my eyes as glaring lights and death stared me in the face. Suddenly, the truck slowly backed up, turned around, and stopped in the center of the road. I kept my eyes focused on it. Within moments, it finally drove off in the opposite direction.

I stood in the pouring rain, scared out of my mind and shaking like a leaf. I could not believe the ordeal I had just experienced. I never saw anything like that before.

Eric Richards, a very troubled man, was out for blood. His thinking was way over my head and I had absolutely no idea what to do or how to get away from him. Every part of my being came unglued as my eyes remained fixed on the rear lights of the pickup truck.

As hard as the rain fell, I still felt the warmth of my tears trickle down my cheeks. I slowly walked back to the car, slid into the driver's seat, placed my hands over the steering wheel, and rested my head on them. I thanked God I was alive.

I closed my door, put the car in gear, and turned my car around. All kinds of thoughts went through my mind. I had another brush with death: it was really scary. No one ever knows when his or her number is up. To die at the hands of a maniac was far beyond my imagination. Eric Richards was a thorn in my side, which I could not get out.

He had bad character without remorse or a conscience about what he had put me through. He had absolutely no feeling for anything, as reflected in his eyes, which were stone cold. The man had no apathy and lacked sorrow and repentance. I thought T. J. Masterson was incorrigible, but Eric Richards lacked any appropriate emotional response. He was completely insensitive about life.

I took a deep breath and recollected my thoughts. I focused on the roadway and saw the freeway lights ahead. I was so happy to see civilization again. As I made my way onto the freeway and continued to drive I-5 South back to Los Angeles.

Everything was quiet on the freeway. In fact, the freeway was empty. I drove for hours, which seemed like an eternity. My gas gauge did not look too good, and I prayed a gas station would appear.

What a long stretched of highway—miles and miles of stretched out nothingness.

All that was visible were the long white lines painted on the black asphalt. Hours passed, and the only thing I heard was the night sounds coming in. Being alone out there, the littlest sound made me jump out of my skin.

I had time on my hands, too much time. To not go stir crazy, I started humming. That night seemed to last forever. I was wrapped up in my thoughts when seasons of my life started to flash before me.

"Mary, you've been nothing, but a curse! I'm putting you in reform school!" my mother shouted.

"Stop, Mom, please stop," I pleaded.

"Your brother should've lived instead of you . . . I never wanted you!"

Cry, cry, and cry . . . All I did was cry. The brokenness inside ripped through me and tore my heart apart. I never belonged; even my mother's people did not want me.

"You're your father's daughter. Why your mother had you, we'll never understand!"

I was a little girl, knee-high to my mother's hip, and I had been told I was a mistake by everyone. However, God loved me and because of that I was going to make it.

So many chapters ran through my mind, I cringed at the thought of those bad seasons of my life. For some reason or another, perhaps because of the way I felt, I drew negativity. I tore myself apart and as I continued to drive, I sobbed like a baby.

"God, help me. It can't end like this," I cried.

I hated all that time on my hands as I travelled that vast, open stretch of highway. I relived moments in my life as I rode in the middle of nowhere.

I had everything a little girl ever wanted. A poor little rich girl, who had all the treasures of the world and went places others only wished to visit. I had everything, except the love and affection of my mother. At the age of six, my little world disappeared.

That big old sixteen-room Victorian house back on Essex Avenue was filled with memories. If its walls could talk, it would fill pages with the feelings of my heart.

"You're my special little girl," Uncle Jerry said. "Come lie with me."

The stench of his old, chewed up cigar; his hideous laugh, body odor, face, and that terrifying look in his eyes. He was twisted and demented.

I wept that lonely night as I drove on the long stretched of highway. I still felt the awesome pain of rejection and betrayal. I went from bad to worse and kept jumping from the frying pan to the fire.

Will I ever learn? Will it ever stop?

"Finally, a gas station, thank God!" I said aloud.

I pulled into the station and up to the pump. I filled my tank with gas, quickly paid the attendant, got back into my car, and continued to drive. Everything was so quiet out there; the freeway was so deserted.

It was almost daybreak when I saw the dawn come up. The road became clearer. I was close to Los Angeles, which was a relief because at one point I thought I had gotten lost. The freeways were too complicated and at night it was even worse.

I was finally on the right road. I saw the sign for Los Angeles and took a deep breath, a sigh of relief. I knew it was just a matter of time before I arrived.

I finally reached Los Angeles, and shortly thereafter I drove down Market Street in Lennox.

What a welcomed sight!

I drove to Rosie's and Bill's house and stay there until they came home. I was so exhausted, my eyes burned like fire and hurt every time I blinked. Every part of my body was stiff and ached. I sat in their living room by the big window. I thought about my family back home, and bridges burned so badly. My life was a total disaster; what I tried to do seemed to have blown up in my face. I guess T. J. Masterson won.

Stop thinking these thoughts! Shame on you, you've come too far to call defeat!

Negative thinking was one thing from which I tried to stay away. I made it a rule of thumb to trust in God, believe in myself, and dare to dream. I had reached a fork in the road. I could not go straight because I would hit a brick wall. I had to either bear right or left. Since I was unsure about which direction I should go, my faith kicked in.

After I sat for a while, I fell asleep. Hours must have passed because when I looked up, Rosie and Bill had arrived.

"Mary, what happened?" Bill asked. "Why didn't you wait for us?"

"Are you all right?" Rosie asked.

"I'm okay, just tired," I replied.

We sat in the kitchen for hours as I recounted my horrific experience. As I told the story, chills went up and down my spine as I recalled the silver pickup truck, those bright high beams on me, and death reaching for me. I described the blackness of night, the pouring rain, flashes of lightning across the sky, and the sounds of thunder.

I truly did not know how I made it. Yet, I was in one piece because God had looked out for me. Deep inside lies my inner child, a little girl scared out of her mind, wondering when death would find her.

Eric Richards—a troubled, twisted, and unbalanced individual—had done everything, but rip me apart. Physically, I was physically alive, but mentally and emotionally torn to shreds. Eric knew exactly what he was doing. He tried his best to make a statement in my life. I had not bargained for that. I did not go straight out asking for trouble, but unfortunately trouble found me.

I've got to pray for a way out.

I felt like I was encased in a tomb. Walls of stone had been erected all around me. I was trapped in that chapter and could not breathe. My mind, body, and soul were engulfed in such horror and a fear that made my heart pound, flutter, miss beats, and skip totally out of rhythm.

I lie awake every night as a cold sweat poured down my body and my hands got clammy. Truly, I did not know what the outcome of that chapter would be, or if I would survive at all. I was back in Los Angeles and had to move on, with fear or no fear. I refused to stay a prisoner in my life. I would not be pushed over the edge.

I made a lot of changes when I returned from up north and even put in for a shift change at work. I did not care which bus line I drove, but I preferred driving on day shifts rather than nights.

I had never known such fear. Even with T. J., my fear was more about his temper than his mind. Back then, I had somewhere to run and good friends to confide in. In California, I walked alone without the closeness I had with friends back in New Jersey.

Even though Rosie and Bill, Jane and Earl, and Arthur were there for me, I was still withdrawn. I did not want to reveal my heart; pieces of me found it difficult opening up to anyone when I felt trapped and confined.

I kept those feelings to inside for fear of being judged and ridiculed. My feelings were much different back in New Jersey. Jane, Liz, and I had a seemingly unbreakable bond. I had known them for years; we went through a lot together. It was so easy for us to open up to each other. We did not feel inferior and never gave it a second thought when we bore our souls.

I had always been very critical of myself; my worst enemy. In California, I did not have a chance to bond with anyone in quite the same way. However, whatever we shared was something special. Yet and still, I kept my feelings to myself.

True friendship is a garden filled with beautiful endearments, sentiments, and love. Every flower that grows in the garden is a true gift from God, a very precious and irreplaceable act of love.

I welcomed and embraced my friends. I cherished what Arthur and I had. I valued the love that was shown to me and deeply appreciated what we shared. I did not know how I was to get through that chapter of my life. Emergence from that tomb seemed impossible.

For twenty years I was with T. J., which was a good amount of time to know someone. However, with Eric I had only spent nine months—what a difference, like night and day.

How stupid was I to think in such a short period of time I'd have a meaningful relationship with someone I'd share my life with, but not know him better?

That entire chapter brought me so much pain and sorrow. Being with Eric had torn me apart.

Where is that man's mind? How far does his understanding go? Can he be reasoned with?

I had questions on top of questions. My mind mirrored what I saw in front of me: a face of fear had been embedded by a twisted, troubled mind. Whatever Eric was going through, it had overflowed into mine. I was a captive of the unresolved issues of his life. Only he held the key to the horror of that nightmare brought. Eric had a closed, narrow mind. He refused to comprehend; things were either his way or no way.

I did not like to be controlled. I did not want to be a prisoner in my life. Exactly what that man tried to do, I was unsure, but I knew he was not going to win.

I had travelled too far to be entangled in another person's madness. I wanted a clean break—a fresh, new start. The goals I had set would be accomplished. My past would not be repeated.

The chapters of what was became a total disaster. The seasons of the years gone by had brought much pain in other people's lives. Worlds were destroyed, hearts had been broken, and lives were torn apart. My days of long ago were comprised of wrong turns and bad decisions.

At sixteen I was desperate to get out from under the twisted and demented world of Uncle Jerry. Yet, I choose a road that turned into self-destruction. Twenty years later, I remained on the run from another chapter of horror.

That crazy night on that slippery freeway brought back so many horrific memories. Scared out of my mind, I wondered if that night I had once again escaped death.

How do you run from death? How many chances do we get? Will death catch up with me?

Thoughts like that had to stop. God had not brought me out for death to overtake me. What I tried to do would have failed, and then my mother and T. J. would have won. I could not let Eric Richards get the best of me. I had to survive.

I had overcome so much. God had certainly been good to me. When I looked back on those days gone by, so much opens up to me. Those earlier chapters of Mommy and me left me wondering why she could not love me. I escaped ten wretched years of Uncle Jerry's twisted, demented world in which he had imprisoned me. The hard years of T. J. and me had been survived. Yet, I was not torn apart or destroyed.

During part three of *From Darkness to Dawn*[3], worlds had been taken from me, yet somehow I found the strength to get back on my feet and move on. I had travelled many roads since then. After all I had been through I dared not think Eric Richards was going to take me out.

I would not give up because I had come too far to turn back. My faith in God and my will to survive had brought me through. That chapter was written to end. After that, a new chapter began.

---

3 Adams, *From Darkness to Dawn.*

CHAPTER 11

Dead Calm

Time moved on. The anticipation of the unexpected was enough to drive me crazy. I danced on the edge of time, and was confused and beside myself. I stayed on an emotional rollercoaster, but life had to go on.

I had to move forward and not allow Eric to cripple or paralyze me to the point where I could not move on. I returned back to work and did what I had to do to continue to live my life. Life had to get better; things had to change; it could not linger as it had forever.

Arthur and I started dating. It felt good to be with him. In fact, I smiled and projected more. I began to focus on my future.

Crushed under the weight of chapters gone by, my inner child still cried out to me. I was transparent. Even my grandmother in Portugal back in the 1950s saw the child within. Even Arthur saw my pain and empathized with my hurt. He, too, saw my inner child.

As my tears continued to fall, I was so grateful I had someone to share my feelings with—I no longer had to be alone. The new chapter that was about to begin was ready to be written. Pages awaited the pen to write and anxiously continue the story of my life.

Eric Richards was still out there somewhere. I knew even the police could not help me. That man was so elusive; no one knew where he was.

I had to remain afloat and maintain my sanity. This darkness that surrounded me could not overtake me; I had to fight back. I was tangled in a vicious web that was weaved because of my vulnerability.

Arthur had been great and very supportive. He kept me from going over the edge.

"Angel, move in with me. I'll protect you," he said.

I truly believed him and knew he really cared. Because of that, he made my days a bit more tolerable, despite that horrific nightmare.

Days passed and I gave moving in with Arthur much thought. I decided to do it. Many nights I lay awake and thought about my future, and about how Arthur would be a part of it. That man was the center of my thoughts and conversations. He brought great joy into my life.

I thought about how perfect my life could be and it put a smile on my face. As I sat on the blue couch by the patio doors, I embraced the brightness of the moon as it peaked through the white curtains in Arthur's living room. I took a deep breath of relief and embraced feelings I had not felt in years. It was as though God had smiled down on me.

Fall was moving in, and I saw the sky change. Clouds began to appear with their grey tones. Even the briskness of the air was sharp and similar to a bite of the early mornings. Many days I sat out on Arthur's balcony to enjoy the warmth of the afternoon sun. In the evenings, the two of us sat under the beautiful night sky and projected our future.

It felt like a dream come true. God certainly had a sense of humor. Twenty-five hundred miles away and clear across the

Rockies, the man I had met back in 1976 was about to change my life forever.

Eight years later, destiny had found me. For once in my life, I did not look for love because love had found me.

Days passed and everything was quiet. It was a dead calm. Every stop I pulled into with the bus, I looked around for trouble. Every corner, street, and layover I prepared for the unexpected. I did not trust Eric or put anything past him.

That man was a time bomb waiting to go off. It became harder to work at the transit division because my runs were constantly switched. Being on the extra board made things more difficult because my runs came in later.

One Wednesday evening, I had the Jefferson Boulevard bus line; my bus was packed—standing room only. It must have been around 3:15 pm, when I thought I saw Eric standing by the bus stop among waiting passengers. I cringed at the thought of stopping.

I pulled in and opened the door. As the passengers boarded the bus, Eric was in the center of the line.

"Hello, operator, how are you doing?" he asked.

He had a smug look on his face. Throughout the trip, I ran cold and hot as shooting pain went through the back of my neck.

Get a grip. He's trying to scare you, but you can't let him intimidate you.

Eric was a complete madman, who was out of control. My head pounded as a result of tremendous pressure. Every time I tried to take my mind off of him, the devil showed up.

"What am I going to do? He won't quit," I said to myself.

He just sat and stared out the window. There was an empty look on his face, as if there was no life behind them. We rode up and down Jefferson Boulevard, and not a word came out of his mouth. My stomach was in knots and my hands were cold and clammy. I felt like I was going to pass out.

When I arrived at Huntington Park, there were only three passengers left, including Eric.

"Last stop, everybody off," I said.

A man in the white shirt got off at the back, and a lady and her little girl walked up to the front.

Before she got off the bus, I yelled, "Sir, you get off the bus, too!"

Eric did not expect me to do that. He reluctantly got up, shot me a deadpan stare, and went out the back stairwell. I was about to pull off when I heard the church bell chime: nine o'clock. I felt a bit relieved.

All the way back to the bus garage, I kept was aware of things around me and did not take my eyes off the road. I knew Eric Richards was out there. A couple of blocks before I reached the division, his black Camaro pulled alongside the bus. I saw him in my right side mirror, blinking his headlights.

Oh no, what am I going to do?

Eric swung his car in front of the bus, which caused me to stop suddenly. He opened his door and shouted obscenities at me. It was the wee hours of the morning and there was not a soul in sight.

That crazed man stood in the middle of Van Ness Avenue and acted like a lunatic. I called for assistance and within moments I saw the lights of the transit police approach. Eric got back into his car, turned it around, and drove off.

A sense of calmness washed over me because for once he had not gotten the best of me. Maybe something inside of me had awakened. Perhaps, I had received my second wind. Regardless, I refused to go down without a fight. I had been a fighter all my life and this man fed off of my fear. He actually got off on it.

I finally pulled into the yard and all sorts of questions went thrown me. I had to file an incident report. When I was through I got into my car and drove home. I was not going to let Eric

Richards bring me down. I had left me wide open and that man took full advantage of it.

He was deranged and needed to be admitted to a psyche ward. I was going to turn thirty-six soon and had not used the brains with which I was born.

How had I been taken in again?

I only blamed myself; no one pushed me into that mess. I stepped into territory way over my head. I had no business stepping into it and needed to fight for my life to get out of it. Arthur, Rosie, nor Bill could help me; I had to work that chapter out myself. Not even the police could do anything because Eric Richards was too slick, even for them.

I had no scars or bruises. There was absolutely no evidence of Eric's abuse, but bouquets of black roses tied in black satin ribbons. It was a reminder of his sick, demented love for me, which I could take me to my grave.

My life up until that point had been very hard. Although there were times when I wanted to give up, I kept thinking about my children. Dying would leave them with so many unanswered questions and those kids would never know how much I loved them or what I had gone through to make a new beginning.

As I prayed, I believed God would see me through and give me beauty for ashes one day. As I tried to get out of that awful nightmare, I lost so much valuable time. I hated it.

Fall had set in and the leaves began to dangle on tree branches. As I sat under the fall sky, the briskness of autumn was evident and a breeze gently blew my hair. I could not begin to count the hours I had sat out in the backyard and embraced the beauty around me. I thought about Arthur and me. As I watched the tiny little sparrows eat sunflower seeds, I thanked God for my life.

Arthur also had a great love for life and appreciation for things around him. I was so very blessed to have someone with whom to share my life—a man who loved what I love. With that, life was so much brighter, better than if I had been loved by someone who was the total opposite of me.

I owe so much of my level of gratitude to the earlier years of my life: the years of Mommy and me. I watched her love God's creatures and extend her hand to those in need. Her love for life was amazing. Although stricken with a broken heart, the love my mother extended to others—including animals—was cherished and admired.

My one wish was for her to show me some of that love. As I watched her love others, somehow it seemed she loved me. Even though some of those chapters of my life were heart-wrenching and still brought me to tears, I considered them dear. I never understood why my Mommy did not love me—perhaps, it was better left unsaid.

No one ever tried to explain her aversion to me. Her distance caused so much of me hurt. A big part of me had died, but no matter how I felt, my life had to go on. Somehow, I found the core of my existence and from there moved forward. I had to be set free and cease punishing myself.

The answers I looked for faded; my mother remained still light-years away. My heart ached as I tried to find peace. Even though a new chapter was about to begin, I held on to the possibility of a miracle.

As I enjoyed the moments around me, I was so grateful to be alive and embraced that new chapter. I welcomed it with an open mind and receiving heart.

"Angel, where are you?" Arthur asked.

I guess I was caught up in my little world of reflection, so I did not hear Arthur when he came in.

"Out here, Arthur," I replied.

He and I sat under the beautiful sky and shared our dreams and expectations. With Arthur, I was able to be open and free; I had never felt that way. The days he and I sat out back in the beautiful garden under the gorgeous pine tree were countless. We drank lemonade and ate cookies. We shared stories about our lives and laughed like teenage sweethearts.

Days were shorter. Even at 7:00 pm, the backyard was still lit by the sun. I sat out there for hours gathering pinecones that had fallen on the ground. With a wicker basket in one hand, and garden gloves in the other, I gathered and placed them in a beautiful, huge, floral ginger jar that stood in front of the fireplace.

Those days were beautiful. Everything within me felt safe and good. I became stronger. Some negative feelings I had began to clear. I started to regroup and had time to think to take in the good and cast out the bad. I used those thoughts to my advantage and concentrate on how to end the Eric catastrophe.

Chapters past had taken a toll on me. I was worn out and tired. At times there was a smile on my face, but a great part of me hid behind that smile. Although outgoing and assertive, in my personal life I was very private and did not reveal too much about me.

A keepsake diary, which captured years of the chapters of my life, had never been written. That part of my life lived within me, only to be revealed during another season in time. I looked deep within my heart, embraced my feelings, and kept them under lock and key. I feared no one would understand me.

Life was truly beautiful and God had given me another chance at life! I was truly grateful. I realized everything I had been through were building blocks for my future. Those chapters had shaped and molded my character to become the woman God had intended. That shy, timid, sixteen year old girl—who ran from fear—had gone through the school of hard knocks. She had matured.

It was not where I had come from that mattered. It was where I had been and the experiences that made or broke me. It was my way of thinking, my attitude, and the choices I had made.

What we learn is gleaned from the chapters we have lived. How we go through them determines if we win.

Life changes like the wind and nothing is predictable. Although we get weary and may sob an ocean of tears, the lessons we learn are very valuable. We mature through the lessons we live.

I was truly grateful to be alive. God had definitely looked out for me. That chapter of Eric and me had to end. Before I could move forward, I had to get control; Eric had to become a thing of the past.

I stood on the edge of time and felt myself slip away. I could not lose my footing; I would fall off and die. I could no allow that chapter to defeat me; I had to survive.

I cried in my sleep and woke with tear-filled eyes. Things were so uncertain and I was in a tailspin. I pondered many questions and wondered when that chapter would end. I was in the middle of a bad decision and regretted another chapter that had gone bad.

I could not move forward until I had cleaned up my act. I had been on automatic pilot for quite some time and feverishly tried to catch my second wind. That chapter was crazy; Eric was crazy. The stillness, the quiet, motionless hush, a dead calm. To think Eric Richards had faded into the sunset would be foolish and stupid on my part.

Spine-chilling, eerie feelings of that crazy period had robbed so much of my life. I was at a standstill; my feet seemed to be stuck in the mud. I worked things out in my mind and stayed ahead of the game while I anticipated my next encounter with Eric.

It was such a dead calm, like the eye of a hurricane: so still, so scary. I never knew when the craziness would start again; I was trapped in the center of an explosive situation. Yet, I was ready to fight back.

Days passed, and things between Arthur and me got better. The situation with Eric had brought us closer and made our relationship stronger. Everything was so wonderful, and I felt so complete. Despite dealing with Eric, there was a part of me that was truly at peace with Arthur.

Why is life full of adversity? Why are the roads we travel often painful? Is there a purpose for the seasons we live through?

These questions were what my mind contemplated. Wisdom was the book of experience, taught by the school of hard knocks. The heart-wrenching seasons of my life placed me in awe and complete amazement. The seasons I had gone through made me the woman God had intended to emerge.

There was no doubt God had been with me. Even through that crazy season of my life, God had His hand on me. I had allowed another man to charm his way into my life. He was well-dressed and carried a Bible; I was taken in. We went to church together, sang in choir, and every Friday evening, he had Bible study at his house. Eric was a pillar of strength well-loved in his church and community.

Months before we dated, Eric took me everywhere and bought me everything. The lifestyle he led was that of the rich and famous: a fifteen-room house in Palos Verdes, a yacht, champagne and fine wines. We dined in the most exclusive restaurants. The lights, glitter, and glamour—I was enamored by that man. Eric was a smooth talker; his words swept me off my feet.

That same man was stalking me and had me running for my life. That chapter, coupled with those prior, was written in the far corners of my mind and lay in a state of stillness as I recovered from them. Eric Richards was too much for me, definitely someone I did not want to deal with.

In that period of dead calm, I may have been down for the count, but I was not out. I would rise again.

CHAPTER 12

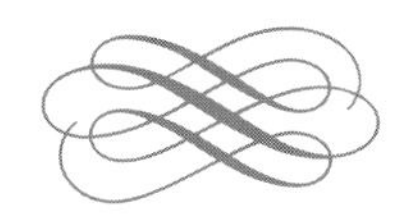

Change of Events

Everything seemed to run smoothly, except my relentless nightmare: Eric. He was like a bad dream and everything about him spelled trouble. In the shadows of the night, the darkest part of the evening, unimaginable thoughts ran through my mind and I wonder how my life became so out of control.

A part of me wanted to go back to New Jersey really badly. I wanted to catch the next midnight flight and leave that crazy nightmare behind. I knew in my heart if I could not wish that catastrophe away, I had to keep it at bay. I would not let it swallow me up, or I might have been lost in the devil's entrapment.

I wished I could close my eyes and wish Eric away, but that was virtually impossible. Something had to be done. I wanted to make California my home and break new ground so my children and I could be a family again. I promised myself when I left New Jersey I would return to them one day. Although my mother and I were worlds apart, she was still my mother, and I loved her very much.

That chapter of my life had to get better. Sooner or later, Eric Richards had to give up. Somehow, that horrendous chapter of my life would come to an end. As everything happened around me, I still tried to call back home.

The reality of what once was became a memory or two. The life I so loved seemed to be whisked away like fallen leaves swept away by the harsh winds of a winter day. It was devastating—the ones I loved were far from me.

Call after call, I kept calling that number. All my attempts were fruitless and all that remained was a prayer and song.

My mother was in control. She did what she wanted and refused to do what she had no desire to do. I knew how far I could go when I insisted on my rights.

Why do I put myself in harm's way? Why do I leave myself open to a world of hurt?

Why I allowed myself to be a target of my mother's frustration, I would never know. At thirty-something, I still drowned in the same tears shed by that little girl on Essex Avenue—alone and scared.

"Mom, that's not fair," I complained.

"I wish you were never born, Mary. God should've taken you instead of my sons! Why I had you I'll never know," she replied.

Her words cut through my heart and her voice tore me apart. Reliving those seasons of my life opened up wounds of my mother's loveless feelings toward me. I craved her love and wanted to reclaim the many years wasted between us.

Nothing had changed. Once again, my mother shut the door in my face. The relationship between my mother and me was still strained. Our conversations left a lot to be desired. Like a domino effect, the pieces fell.

My world, life, and sanity seemed to have given way to a pool of nothingness. I had left behind bits and pieces of my shattered world and fallen facedown in doubt and uncertainty. A great part of me was numb to the reality, which surrounded me.

Chapters already written had come back into play and taunted me. My mother's resistance to show love toward me hurt badly. My heart numbed as the very ones who were supposed to love me, betrayed me. I was not even halfway through my life and had cried an ocean of sorrows. My heart had buckled under the crushing weight of the chapters lived.

The pieces of my life were like a huge puzzle scattered all over the floor with no beginning or end. The thought of being so disconnected frightened me; it drove me insane. No matter how I felt, life had to go on. If I did not keep moving, I was going to be lost among the rubble and ashes.

The division manager put me on the Miller Street run, which was one of the worst runs. From Monday to Friday, I kept my eyes open for Eric Richards to pop up. With much thought behind my actions, I knew I was one step ahead of him. That is, until one Friday night around 8:00 pm, when Eric Richards stood in the midst of passengers who waited to board my bus.

He stared at me, and then said, "Hello, operator. Where have you been? Long time no see."

I cringed at the sight of him. It was like facing the devil, an open book of catastrophic events mixed with insanity. Eric Richards is a madman in disguise.

That same eerie went up and down my spine. Where I had to drive was much too dangerous for Eric to be with me because Miller Street ran through very bad sections of Los Angeles. Most of its lines ran through abandoned factories and open fields.

Unfortunately, my radio was not working, so I was in a catch-22. Everyone exited my bus, except Eric. He sat in the back, motionless. Not a word came out of his mouth. I was at Miller Street and 104th Street with no way of getting him off the bus.

I quickly got up and tried to run out the door, but he was too fast for me. He rushed to the front of the bus, grabbed me, pushed me down, and then wedged me between the fair box and the driver's seat.

"Where do you think you're going, my dear?" he hissed. "If hell be for real, I'm going to take you down there with me."

From afar, I saw bright lights. I leaned on my horn and prayed somebody heard me. Suddenly, I heard a truck pull up from behind the bus. Eric froze. Then, he slowly let me go and reached to open the bus door.

"I'm not through. I'll be back," he warned.

I could not catch my breath. I was terrified as I watched Eric run through the field and jump over a barb wire fence. I wanted to scream, to shout. Eric had proven he was crazy and not about to give up. I finished my run and when I arrived at my next stop, two elderly ladies boarded the bus.

"Dear, someone left flowers on the seat," one lady said.

I got up and walked back to where the ladies stood. Lying on the seat was a single black rose and a heart made of black construction paper. The words in red ink read: I love you.

I knew the items had been left by Eric, but I did not say a word. I went back to my seat and continued my run. When I arrived at my layover, fear took a hold of me. I sat under the dark and isolated freeway bridge. The area looked scary.

As I rendered the bus out of service, Eric ran toward the bus. I quickly drove off. About 1:30 am in the midst of waiting passengers at Normandie Avenue and 73rd Street, Eric pushed his way through and boarded the bus. I drove up and down the avenue for hours. When my last passenger got off, he sat behind me and stared out the side window.

Before I could say a word, Eric was in my face. He grabbed my arm, and I felt a pinch. I could not get out of his grip. Then, everything blurred. There was absolute silence.

My life had come to a complete standstill. All I heard was the faint beat of my heart. I was at the mercy of darkness and eerily anticipated Eric's return. Suddenly, I heard voices outside the bus.

"Operator, are you all right!" a lady shouted.

I was unable to move and could not answer her. Yet, I sensed a faint scream for help come from within me. Everything looked fuzzy and distorted. Like a bad dream, nothing seemed normal.

Suddenly, someone picked me up and carried me to a nearby car. It took me time to regain my balance. Before we arrived at the hospital, I recognized my supervisor from the Miller Street run was driving his designated car.

"Thank you, Jim," I said.

While I sat in the waiting room, thoughts of catastrophic proportions ran through my mind. I was running from the shadow of an elusive man like a phantom in the night. No one, but me saw him, as he lurked in the darkness and waited for me. Eric Richards scared me.

I was ashamed and fearful. I did not know what to say. When Arthur came to take me home, I remained silent. I went deep into my thoughts and separated from reality. I ran far, far away. I would have run to the ends of the earth.

That had been a difficult night; every part of me hurt. I was devastated and crushed. My mind, body, and soul were weighed down by the pain and sorrow of my brokenness. I withdrew so deep within that I was placed back in Mama's foyer on Essex Avenue. I stood in front of my mama's huge Venetian mirror and admired the beautiful, multi-colored stained glass window behind me.

In simpler days—those lazy, carefree days of long ago when I had tea parties with Miss Molly and Mr. Bear and took many walks through Hatfield Park with Daddy and Sporty—I spent hours sitting under the beautiful sycamore tree. I ate Mama's home-baked cookies and drank her orange cream. My mind took me back to where I choose to be as an escape from the hell I lived in.

God, being as gracious as He is, always seemed to take me to a new level to, perhaps, help maintain my sanity. I knew beyond a shadow of a doubt, I should have lost my mind back then. Yet, God has a purpose for me. Even though my birth was not a timeless treasure to my mother, God does not make mistakes.

What the devil meant for evil, the Lord turned things around to the good. So, when that day finally comes, I wanted to be able to move on with my life.

"Angel, I love you," Arthur said.

A part of my world had been painted in colors of the rainbow. Beautiful glorious pastels, some colors even shimmered and glowed. Yet, there was still a big part of my life that was tainted in smeared tears I had shed.

A great part of my heart was tattered, like an old book with shredded, torn pages yellowed from years gone by. I sat on the edge of time, in the quietness of my surroundings, lost in the silence of my broken heart.

When Arthur and I arrived home, I took a long, hot shower. Then, I poured myself a warm glass of milk, went to sit on the glider in the gazebo, and awaited daybreak. It was glorious out there: the sun began to rise over the huge cluster of pine trees by the old wooden shed. At the tip of the sycamore trees, I saw birds flutter their little wings, as they greeted the morning with songs of praise.

Chimes clung in soft array, as if angels' wings had touched them to greet the new day. My eyes clouded and I got choked up.

I found it difficult to even enjoy the new season in my life. I was trapped in that vicious chapter of Eric and me. I drowned in my tears.

Morning arrived, and I had to collect my thoughts.

Something has to be done.

In desperation, I went to the police station.

"Miss, do you have any proof of what you're saying?" the sergeant asked.

No scars, no bruises, no nothing. Eric's very slick; he knows exactly what he's doing.

"No, sir," I replied.

"I'm sorry, there's nothing I can do," he said, "but please be careful."

Like in Caldwell Hills, once again I was left to fend for myself. For years I searched for answers. Countless nights, I twisted and turned. I would beat myself up because I had allowed me to be entrapped by a madman.

My entire life had left a lot to be desired. The times I fell flat on my face were countless. Yet, for all the times I slipped and fell, my Lord was right there beside me. The devil could not take me out.

Dr. Jekyll and Mr. Hyde he had many disguises. Eric always seemed to be two steps ahead of me. God knew he tried to checkmate me, but regardless of Eric's horrific manipulation, I knew my miracle was only a prayer away. The line between sanity and insanity had narrowed; I was on the verge of a nervous breakdown.

If I had given in to my emotions and allowed my thoughts to give way to my heart, I would have been doomed. The only way I stayed afloat was to pray, believe, and focus on the cross no matter how hard and ugly things seemed, My only hope was in God, I would survive.

When my shift began, I drove up and down Hawthorne Boulevard. My head throbbed from the chaos and madness I was caught up in.

Where do I go from here, Lord? I seem to go from bad to worse with no end in sight to this craziness.

I was in a state of shock as my life seemed to drift further into the abyss. Disaster awaited me as I was blind-sided and side-swiped on a collision course. I would have thought I would have gotten it right by that time. I was filled with mixed emotions while my heart was weighed down by doubts and fears.

I ran from the past into the devil's hands. While my unsettled heart yearned for the world I had left behind: pages of unending pain and lines of broken promises. My heart grieved and was pulled apart; I wondered if I would ever have peace in my life.

I had steered me in the wrong direction. Not once had I given way to God. I lied to myself and broke my promise to me. For all the years I put myself in harm's way, instead of thinking before I leaped, I went straight from the frying pan into the fire. I could not climb out.

It seemed I had learned absolutely nothing. Chapter pages kept turning and lines of empty pages waited for writing, yet I had a passion to complete my story life. I knew I had to pull myself up and move on. I had to get back on track and take back control of my life.

Eric Richards would not cripple me, and my life would not paralyze me. I could not allow fear to have its way with me; I had to stay strong. The devil tried to push me over the edge, but he was not going to win. For every mountain I had climbed and every valley I had crossed, I paid a big price. I had walked ten thousand miles, stubbed my toes, and bruised my knees.

That edge of the cliff drew me closer, but no matter how engulfed in fear I was, my God had saved me. It was not by my strength or might, for I was nothing. I knew God, and God alone, would turn my life around. The Lord had certainly been my help and carried me through the darkest times. If time could speak, it would surely testify about the goodness of God in my life.

Life had been very hard for me ever since I was a little girl back on Essex Avenue. However, when that light at the end of the tunnel began to fade, the Lord faithfully awoke me to a brand new day. Those chapters still brought tears, which lay in a dormant state, to my eyes as I prayed for a miracle.

Lines would be written, stories would be told, and pages kept turning as chapters continued to unfold. I had but one life to live, so with passion and desire, I continued to run my race. Somewhere in time, God unfolded a beautiful ending He had created a long time ago.

CHAPTER 13

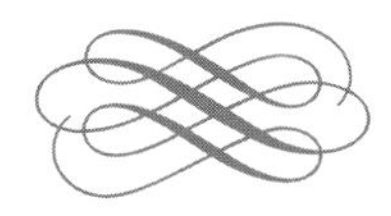

On My Knees

For years I had gone around in circles, never knowing from day-to-day where my life was headed. My entire being was wiped out. What a web I had woven, and, once again, its thin silk strains had entrapped me as prey and awaited my demise. My life had become so complex, so twisted, that most times that craziness seemed an endless journey of nothingness.

"God, help me!" I cried out.

Down under I wandered in darkness as I tried to make sense of it all.

How did I get into another mess? I'm an accident waiting to happen. Perhaps, I have a death wish.

I had strayed so far from the truth and had taken my eyes off the Lord. I had fallen into a pool of vomit and deeper into the pit. I was totally helpless; my sanity hung by a thin thread. I prayed for God to get me through that chapter of my life. The miles I had travelled cost me everything, I was no closer to victory than I was when I started my journey; yet, the grace of God kept me sane.

Days passed and Eric still made my life miserable. Each day seemed to log another entry in that horror story. My move to California had been a quick decision; it was made overnight.

During the miles travelled, I ran from one bad situation to the next, and I faced a brick wall yet again. There seemed to be no way out, but God always rescued me.

Now what?

I feared I was going to self-destruct and sent up prayer after prayer. I even prayed in my sleep. In the stillness of my midnight hours, I found some peace. I sat at the edge of my bed, wrapped in my green quilt, and looked into the darkness with tear-filled eyes. Dogs barked in the distance and a car or two passed. In the midst of darkness, my heart pounded.

Once again, I was surrounded by my fears and cried out, "Oh, Lord, please help me!"

Every day I wondered when Eric would strike again.

Do I run? Do I go back to New Jersey in defeat? Do I fight back?

Whichever way I chose to go, whatever road I chose to take had to be quick. If I stayed still, I was a sitting duck. Eric was not playing—his plan was to take me out.

Oh! If only I can be free and my mind clear.

I was seemingly in another dimension.

"Mary! Mary! Mary!"

From where had that voice come? Was it a voice from the past or was it the voice of God?

From where it had come, I did not know. My mind was so confused, it scared me. I was on the brink of insanity. I clutched my face, covered my eyes with my hands, and sobbed.

"Oh, God, help me."

Hours passed as tears trickled down my cheeks. I felt as hot as fire as I grasped for air and my emotions ran wild. I taunted myself.

"Mary, you were a mistake and should've died instead of my sons. I should've killed you at birth!"

The voice of my mother cried out and her words cut through my heart. Her meaningless words still took my breath away. My mother's fateful expressions never failed to wound me. They broke me down and crippled me.

Am I a product of her frustration and pain?

Since my journey began, there had been times when I knew I was no closer to the truth or knowing me. I had searched for something, but did not truly know exactly what it was. I had a compulsive need to search for me: a little girl cast out, desperately wandering to find answers to questions.

Can anything good come out of this mess? Is there any place for me, or am I truly a mistake as my mother had said?

I was someone's bad choice, a moment in my mother's life when ripples were made in the water and from that I sprang forth. The repercussion of my senseless life rendered me fruitless. Everything I had ever loved, worked for, or purposed to achieve was ripped from me.

In the blink of an eye, I had been taken down by senseless words without meaning instead of moving forward. I had become caught up in another man's fury and never realized the dramatic effect the past had on my life.

Surrounded by night's stillness, I sensed I was losing my mind as the hour hand slowly inched toward midnight.

Dong! Dong! Dong!

The church bells down the street chimed. For half the night I sat and prayed for the telephone to not ring. I knew it would not take much for Eric to find Arthur's telephone number since it was listed in the telephone directory. All Eric needed was the address. My hands felt sweaty, cold, and clammy; I could not catch my breath like I had a rope tied around my neck.

I cried out, "Oh, God, no! It's taking over my mind, body, and soul!"

Can this be the end, the night Eric will get me? Where's that fool . . . Why doesn't he do it and get it over with?

I heard somebody come up the stairs and held my breath. I clutched my quilt as the footsteps grew closer.

"No, I can't take anymore!" I shouted.

I quickly got up, ran to the other side of the room where a desk was positioned by the window, and waited. I carefully peeked through the white lace curtains, but no one was out there. I thought it was Eric.

Day or night, how does one hide from the boogey man?

In my childhood, I hid in the back of my closet with my knees up to my chest; my arms clutched them for dear life. I kept my eyes closed and rocked back and forth.

I whispered, "Please don't hurt me, not tonight. Please, not tonight."

At thirty-something I still hid and questioned if my nightmare would ever end.

The hours that night seemed to linger without compassion for my mental state. Once more, the cold, eerie darkness had me trapped; I was chained to the terror in my heart.

I watched that blasted telephone on the bed beside me and wondered if that crazy man would taunt me. I had been beaten down, crushed, and splattered all over the floor. These pages of my life flew by as the words of my story were inked. From one chapter to the next, my tale seemed to never ending.

The calm before the storm had an indescribable stillness. I knew I stood in the eye of a hurricane amid a hush—absolute nothingness. The evil I sensed seemed to checkmate me. Every part of me was repulsed by Eric; that man grossly disgusted and offended me. Eric Richards wanted to be the death of me.

I went into the kitchen to pour a glass of warm milk. As I paced back and forth, I wore my body out.

Is it possible none of this is real? Perhaps, if I take a deep breath, I'll wake up.

My eyes filled with tears as I sit back on the bed. Hope was all I had left, even if it was only a mere shred that remained to hold on to my sanity. I wondered and prayed, hoped and believed, all the positive qualities that kept me going. God knew I would not let this chapter destroy me—it would not take me out. I focused on the bright lights in the sky and prayed for a miracle.

How far will this nightmare take me before I wake up?

I was on the brink, the very edge of destruction. I did not want to fall to my death. Frightful and terrified, I gasped for breath at the mere image of that bottomless pit. I was as frightened as that little girl in Mama's attic back on Essex Avenue. Years had changed, but time seemed to have stood still.

I was curled up in old blankets under those old, worn out, wooden steps, hidden from Uncle Jerry. I shivered as teardrops fell down my cheeks and tried to become invisible as I heard his footsteps in the hallway below while he searched for me. Cold, clammy, and frightful feelings washed over me once again.

Ring! Ring! Ring!

That sound drove me crazy. The answering machine picked up, but there was not a sound. Eric was very shrewd and always figured out when I was home alone, particularly since Arthur worked a regular shift, it was not difficult to determine when he was at work.

I knew Eric was somewhere close. Sweat came down my brow and my stomach was upset. I gasped for air as I grabbed the telephone and yanked the wire out of the wall; I threw it across the room.

Get up and get out of here! This time I know he's going to come!

I hurried and packed a few things because I could no longer stay there. Arthur was not able to help me anymore. Eric had gotten his number.

How does that crazy mind of his work? Where do I go? What should I tell Arthur?

I had to get away as fast as possible. Eric lurked in the night shadows and watched every move we made. That weekend I was not supposed to be alone, but Arthur had to go to Sacramento to handle some business. In fact, he had left before daybreak—no one should have seen him leave.

How did Eric know Arthur was gone?

I had set new sails, cross over new ground, and wanted to start a new beginning so badly, but had failed. The clock on the dresser stared back at me while the candles dwindled down to nothing.

At 4:00 am I heard the church bells down the street. I grabbed my things and as I began to leave, I realized there was no place to run. I fell to my knees and sobbed uncontrollably. I had no idea how long I cried, but as the tears fell, daybreak came through. The sun had started to rise over the mountains behind me and I saw light come through my bedroom window. That horrifying night was finally coming to an end.

Last night had been a horror experience, and I had to disentangle me from that demented man. So, I sat back down on the bed to regroup.

I can't go on like this.

I looked up and saw the birds in the courtyard flutter their wings in the fullness of the trees. I also saw the kittens laid out around the water fountain. Life returned to our apartment complex as I heard people talking in the courtyard.

I went into the bathroom and pulled myself together. Then, I grabbed my purse and ran out the door to catch the bus. For hours I rode on Crenshaw Boulevard as I waited for Arthur to return home. Memories flashed before me as I contemplated being in a space considered five hours before midnight. It was a scary place to be: stuck in the middle of nothingness where I was engulfed by numbness.

I was confident Eric could not find me as I rode that bus until nightfall. I presumed Arthur would be back soon. Blackness set in as night had taken hold, I stared out the bus window—it was *déjà* vu.

My reflection was a frightened woman. My heart thumped with fear as the night shadows approached. I spent ten long hours on that bus. The bus headed back to Crenshaw Boulevard and 95th Street. I saw the carport in the distance; the lights were brightly lit.

Arthur's home.

I rushed off the bus and ran toward the apartment complex. Before I reached his door, Arthur was already standing in the doorway.

"Where have you been, angel?" he called out. "I've been worried about you!"

I did not say a word. I ran into his arms and would not let go.

"Angel, are you okay?" he asked. "You're shivering."

"I'm okay now; you're here. Just don't let me go," I cried.

We walked back into his apartment. I suddenly felt as if I was in another world that was safe—a place where no harm would befall me. At Arthur's I had found a safe haven where I was in heaven's rest, surrounded by the love of Jesus.

God had made that moment possible. Instead of angels, I had Arthur with me. For that space in time, I was able to lay my head down to rest.

CHAPTER 14

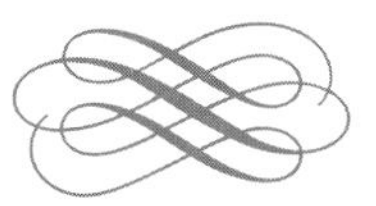

The Black Rose

Everything looked beautiful; it was the time of year I loved the most as I enjoyed when Mother Nature came alive. I embraced the beauty around me and thanked God for my life. In spite of all I was going through, I still enjoyed some of the wonders that came with the seasons.

As the days passed, I started to trim the bushes and planted more tress in the garden. Every day was a new battle with my emotions. Everything within me went through changes as I tried to figure out why I allowed Eric into my life. I had protected me for so long after those chapters with T. J. I was surrounded by the same madness: stuck between the craziness of one man's mind and the viciousness of uncontrollable rage.

I had left me wide open—yes, haste makes waste. Every day I prayed for a miracle: for Eric to fall off the face of the earth. In reality, I knew that it was not going to happen. That chapter had many twists and turns, nothing, but unexpected, unwanted surprises. Eric Richards was definitely not a welcomed sight. Every time I saw that man, I cringed, not knowing what to expect.

My entire existence had become so unbalanced, so upside-down. It seemed I could not get my feet out of the mud, which was discouraging. I was far from where I expected to be; I never dreamed I would be stuck knee-deep in a swamp of fear that surrounded me.

How can a man be so controllable?

Eric knew exactly which buttons to push. He knew how far he could go to scare me. There was nothing funny about the game he had been playing. It was a very dangerous mind game, a confusing, complex composition of one man's distorted, deep-seated issues. Something had taken him over that controls his life. Unfortunately for me, I was at the center of his madness, strangled by the anger and frustration that troubled his mind. There seemed to be no way out.

What do I do? Where do I go? Can anyone help me?

My life should have been lived on the wings of an eagle as I flew to new heights and broke free from the old chapters of my life. Instead, I stood at a standstill. Until my nightmare ended, I remained grounded, unable to go forward or give to anyone. Arthur understood me: he stood in my corner.

"Angel, we have the rest of our lives. I've waited this long, I can wait a little longer," Arthur assured me.

His words meant so much to me. They gave me so much freedom to work my way out of the mess that overwhelmed me.

That weekend Arthur had to travel to Palo Alto to get his grandmother. She had not been feeling well, so he decided she would come live with us. Since, she lived alone he knew she would be better off with us. I was excited about her coming.

When Arthur left I started to clean the apartment. Arthur left early Saturday morning, so I had that weekend to myself. I washed curtains and made up a room for Grandma Blanche. I even painted the walls a soft lavender—one of her favorite colors—and hung a beautiful wooden cross above her bed.

I was so busy, time had escaped me. It must have been around 2:15 pm when I decided to take a break and walk to Alondra Park to feed the ducks. I sat under beautiful, huge eucalyptus trees near the wooden bridge that crossed over a little area in the back of the lake where fluffy white rabbits lived.

The park's serenity was simply heavenly. Its peace and tranquility put my soul at rest. So, I closed my eyes for a while and slept. Hours must have passed because when I woke up, children played and people talked nearby; the park's quietness had ceased to exist. I heard the old church bells chime across the street, next to the ice cream parlor. I could not help but hear those beautiful bells ring.

Dong! Dong! Dong!

The church bells glistened in the sun as they swung back and forth in the huge stone tower. Birds flew overhead and fluttered their wings, making melodies in tune with those gorgeous bells.

I sat beneath the big fir trees and listened to the bells chime; the sound reminded me of simpler days of my life, which I held very dear to my heart. Every precious moment God allowed me to recall those memories. I welcomed them with open arms and a grateful heart.

It was time for me to head home as nightfall was setting in. I saw the sunset; it was a picturesque scene on such a lovely night. It astonished me: such rich colors, a beautiful expression of God's love. I enjoy its beauty. As I looked up, I saw the quarter moon smile at me as though God was telling me everything was going to be all right.

I always had an appreciation for life; everything was a gift from God. I had sat outside under the umbrella of God's love on countless occasions and embraced what I saw. Even back in Caldwell Hills, many mornings my children and I would sit on the front porch to admire the sky and watch the cloud formations float by. How beautiful they seemed.

Those clouds gave an illusion as they opened and parted. They cascaded streams of bright light and looked like a stairway to heaven. I loved good thoughts, especially when my mind was plagued with the problems. I enjoyed looking at God's love in motion; it gave me a sense of peace and a true appreciation for life.

For quite some time, I truly thought I had a death wish. It seemed wherever I went, trouble followed me. I attracted the wrong type of people, but I thank God for the few good souls He sent my way. If they had not come, I have absolutely no idea where I would have been.

I continued my walk home. As I approached Arthur's apartment complex I stayed on my p's and q's. I slowly walked toward the black wrought iron gate. To my surprise, outside by the parking area a black Camaro sat that looked exactly like Eric's. I walked around to the side of the entrance to avoid the car.

"How did he find me?" I asked aloud. "Is that really him? It can't be!"

I walked quickly around the huge metal dumpsters as I headed for the back door. I froze when I heard a loud sound come from behind the carport.

"Oh, God, it's him . . . I knew it!"

My heart pounded and it was hard for me to catch my breath. I was speechless and tried to muffle the words that raced through my mind.

Someone hear me, please hear me! Please someone look out your window and see me!

Suddenly I heard footsteps behind me. I began to run.

"Help, help! Somebody help me!" I shouted.

"Lady, are you all right?" a man yelled.

A tall man dressed in dark coveralls approached me. I stared at him because I could not make out his face.

"Miss, are you all right?" he repeated.

As he came closer, I recognized him. It was Mr. Cramer, the complex's janitor.

What's wrong with me?

"Miss, what's wrong?" he asked. "You're as white as a ghost."

"Someone's following me!" I cried out. "It's my ex-boyfriend; he's going to kill me!"

Mr. Cramer helped me to Arthur's apartment, and then he took his huge black flashlight out of his back pocket and walked up and down the hall to see if he could find him. I stood by the front window as he walked the grounds and clutched the curtains with my right hand as I wondered if Eric Richards was really out there.

"Miss, are you sure you saw someone? It's pretty windy out there. Maybe it's the howling of the winds, and the rustling of the leaves you hear," he suggested.

"I'm so sorry. I feel so stupid. Thank you," I replied.

Even though what Mr. Cramer had said made sense, I knew in my heart it was not the wind or leaves: it was Eric. I shut the drapes in the event he was out there. I made sure everything was secure; I even checked all the windows. I did not miss a thing.

I undressed, took a shower, and then I curled up in the folds of the quilt. I lay on the blue couch and prayed Arthur would call.

That was another long night. The clock on the dining room wall read: 10:00 pm, and the winds blew fiercely through the eucalyptus trees out back. The night made me uneasy as leaves rustled, garbage cans toppled over, and the force of the wind even blew the patio furniture over. I wished Arthur, anybody, would call. The sound of the telephone ringing would be welcomed.

The silence drove me crazy and did not help me to keep my mind off of the fear I felt. Around midnight, I poured a glass of warm milk and sat on the blue couch. I looked out the patio doors to admire the full moon and the clear night the winds had brought.

Suddenly, I heard something at the side of the house. It sounded as though someone had walked over broken twigs by the wood pile, which was near the old wooden barrel under the bedroom window. I was too scared to look. I quietly curled up on the floor between the dresser and the blue chair to avoid casting a shadow from the white candles that burned by the side of the bed onto the white shades that covered the windows. I had forgotten to blow them out.

I'm losing my mind. This is driving me crazy.

It must have been about 2:00 am as the moon illuminated the backyard. I could not see the area where the noise had come from because the porch light next to the huge black barbeque needed a bulb. I quietly got up and tried to call Arthur. Each movement I made brought attention to me. So, I sat quietly as hours passed.

Everything was still. I heard the bus on Crenshaw Boulevard. Then, I decided to get up and call Arthur. After a few rings, he answered the telephone.

"Hello," Arthur said.

"Arthur, Eric is here!" I whispered.

"Are you all right, angel?" he asked with tension in his tone. "Did you call the police?"

"Police, what police?" I snapped. "They're not going to help me; they're not going to believe me!"

Eric was like a phantom that ran in and out of the shadows.

So, what do I tell them? I'm running from the invisible man? Do I tell them the truth: I'm running from the boogeyman?

"If you're not going to call, I'll call," Arthur insisted. "I'll be there as soon as I can. I love you."

After we hung up, I sat back down in the corner and stared up at the window. I no longer heard any movement. The only sound was the wind, twigs breaking, and leaves rustling. After a while, my eyes started to burn, and I did all I could to fight off sleep.

Suddenly, I heard a knock on the front door. I quietly went to the door and looked through the peephole. There stood two police officers. I quickly opened the door.

"Thank God you're here. I believe my ex-boyfriend is out there," I blurted.

They searched the grounds, but found absolutely nothing.

"I'm sorry, miss, there's no one out there," one of the officers said.

I was in a state of limbo as they walked off. I shook my head in amazement because the scenario seemed like *déjà* vu.

Time passed, and I watched the sunrise over the pine trees; the break of dawn appeared. I took a shower and got dressed. I was praying when I heard a knock on the front door. Ever so cautiously, I looked through the peephole, but no one was there. I started to walk away when I heard someone run down the steps to the courtyard.

I ran to the kitchen window and saw a man in a black leather jacket run out the wrought iron gate. I went by the door and pressed my ear up against it to determine if I could hear anyone out there, but I heard nothing. I slowly opened the door. There on the brown doormat was a clear box filled with black roses tied with black satin ribbons.

I picked them up and shut the door quickly. I put the chain back on the door. For the rest of the day I sat on the back patio and prayed for the time to go by as I waited for Arthur to come home.

That was one night I have never forgotten. It was a chapter that certainly left a bad impression. I stared at the box of black roses and seemingly looked into Eric's black heart. Arthur finally came home, and as we sat on the patio, I could not believe my nightmare was even happening. I wished I could close my eyes to make the chaos go away. I was on the edge and felt I was living on borrowed time.

Eric knew people; he was into a lot of things. He was a man who carried a Bible and was a deacon in a church, yet he was so far from being seen as the truth. It was sickening. Eric was the devil. That man had issues that stemmed from the background he came from, which obviously included things much more dangerous. His conscious exhibited a hot iron and his heart was as hard as stone. He definitely needed help.

Eric was a loner, and I did not know much about his family. He did not speak much about his past, yet fortunately for me, I ran into his saxophone player, Tony, on one of my runs going to Hollywood Boulevard. He knew Eric's brother, Mat, from South Dakota very well. For weeks after that, Tony kept in touch with me; he really tried to help me.

Weeks passed, and I finally heard from Mat—Tony had kept his word. Mat met with me and explained Eric's past. He told me about their childhood and how somewhere along the line, Eric's personality had split. He got professional help a long time ago, but he stopped treatment along the way.

Mat continued to tell me how Eric had broken off communication with his family For years he had been on his own. I felt sorry for Eric. Perhaps, since Mat had arrived in Los Angeles, Eric would once again get the help he needed, and things would be better for everyone.

Everything seemed a bit more relaxed after I spoke to Eric's brother. Even Arthur felt more at peace. Life seemed to resume a form of normalcy, so I was able to be me for a change.

I had a few errands to run. I kept on my p's and q's all day as I watched for Eric. When I walked back out to my car, I saw a black Camaro in the parking areas. I walked as quickly as possible to my car. On top of the roof were a bunch of black roses tied with black satin ribbons.

Oh, God, he followed me. How did he find me?

I quickly opened the car door. As I was about to shut it, Eric grabbed the top of the door and stopped me.

"Well, well, Mary, where have you been?" He asked with a sinister look on his face. "You know I've been looking for you."

"Eric, why are you doing this? What do you want?"

"You. I want you. Since you don't want me, I guess we have a problem, don't we?"

"You're sick, Eric. You need help! I spoke to your brother, and he said you need help too," I reasoned. "You can't go on like this forever. You're going to hurt someone!"

"So!" He said with a laughed. "What if I just kill you here?"

"Eric, let go! I'll scream; someone's bound to hear me!" I shouted.

Suddenly, I saw him take something shiny out of his right pocket.

Oh, dear God, it's a knife!

"Eric, you're sick! Don't do anything you'll regret," I pleaded.

My heart pounded, and I felt very faint.

Oh no, I'm losing my senses! Oh no, please God!

I drifted away, and sounds became faint and distant. For a moment, I was turned around and disoriented. Then, my head rested on the steering wheel.

What happened? Am I dead?

Eric was nowhere in sight. When I realized I was not dead, I caught my second wind. I quickly put the keys in the ignition and drove away. When I arrived home, Arthur was there waiting for me. Grandma Blanche was seated on the blue side chair by the glass patio door asleep.

"Angel, are you all right?" he asked. "You look as pale as a ghost,"

"No, I'm not all right . . . Leave me alone!" I shouted as I slammed the bedroom door shut.

Oh no . . . I woke Grandma Blanche!

I opened the bedroom door, found Grandma Blanche, and apologize profusely for making such a ruckus.

"I'm so sorry, Grandma Blanche."

Then, I retreated back into the bedroom. I broke down and cried like a baby. Eric was far worse than T. J. Masterson. Eric was sick; that man was twisted. He was definitely in his world. One that was strange, eerie, and very dangerous.

With everything that happened, Arthur stood by me. Strong and secure, he did not let me down. We took a ride to Dana Point and watched the tide come in. It was a beautiful sight; I watched the each wave crash against those enormous rocks with great force, sweep over the top of them, and then splash onto the blanket of sand beneath me.

The force of nature was awesome. The power behind those waves spoke volumes. The night got colder; there was a brisk chill in the air. As we talked, the roaring sounds of the waves captivated me. That entire night was simply gorgeous, even the brilliance of the full moon. Twinkling lights flooded the sky and made that night delightful. I was lost in Arthur's love.

Cuddled close to his heart and wrapped in his arms, I felt so safe. I did not think of anything, but the beautiful night that surrounded me. As we sat together on that brisk, cool November evening, I embraced his warmth and soaked up the gentleness and quietness of Arthur's love.

"I love you, angel. You're my colonial little doll face,"

I smiled. I never heard such sweet words. Not too often had I recalled sweet endearments spoken to me.

"I love you, too, Arthur Adams."

I had very seldom heard the words: I love you. I remembered many days when I stood in front of my gold vanity mirror, dressed in pretty frilly dresses with my hair tied in satin ribbons. I sang my heart out and danced to the tune of Mama's old Victrola.

What a beautiful time in my life.

"Tea, Miss Annie? Cookies, Mr. Bear? Stop, Sporty, you're pulling Miss Molly's hair," I mused. "Miranda, Lucenda, Lucy, and Jane—how are my little friends today?"

Mama was in the kitchen making her jams and preserves. Daddy was on the back porch drinking wine. It was a great time in my life.

In the chapter of those years and the pages filled with storylines, in the midst of my brokenness, I looked back to earlier years of my life until I disappeared into those seasons of time. I guess that was my only means of escape. Since my life had been as hard as it was, especially that chapter of Eric and me, I embraced those moments if only to disappear for a brief, short while.

I listened to the ocean as the breeze caressed my face. It put me in another time and place. I had become a time traveler; my mind took me back to places I loved to be. The sounds of the ocean reminded me of 1953. It was a calm day, and the waters of the Atlantic were beautiful; the rippling waves and the slapping sounds created as the light breeze touched them, and the white caps as the waves rolled onto the shore.

Mama sat on a red plaid blanket stretched out on the sand. Her long, black, silky hair blew freely in the breeze as she made our picnic lunch. Sporty played in the water with Daddy as I chased the balls in front of me. I heard the laughter and smelled the ocean breeze. Many seasons had come and gone since then, little nuggets of memories I held dear to my heart. Those were simpler, innocent years: the happier days of Mommy, Daddy, and me.

"Angel, are you all right?" Arthur asked.

If only he knew where I had been, Arthur would clearly understand the smile on my face and the glistening light in my eyes. For a brief moment, I was able to escape my nightmare and be truly grateful for the opportunity to step away.

That entire chapter had been very hard, to say the least. My heart was shattered and my thoughts were light-years away. In the midst of my confusion, I thanked God for Arthur's love. It was such a beautiful feeling to have someone to spend my life with. After all those years, I started to plan my future.

That night I wished I could stop the hands of time and place them in a bottle. Since I could not make that happen, I wrote them in the journal of my mind to be cherished through the seasons of time. At thirty-something I had fallen in-love. It was a love I had never experienced, one I had been waiting for all my life.

It must have been about 1:00 am when we went back inside and sat in front of a beautiful fire. We shared hot cocoa and roasted marshmallows. That entire weekend went by so quickly, in fact, too quickly.

When we returned home, Arthur parked the car. The two of us started to walk through the courtyard, when we saw a man in a black jacket run out of the building and down the street. When we got to our front door, there on the doormat lay dozens of black roses tied with black satin ribbons. We stood there speechless. No words were spoken.

Grandma Blanche had stayed at Rosie's and Bill's during our stay at Dana Point. I thanked God she had been spared any exposure to Eric's madness.

"Oh, God, Eric won't quit," I moaned.

"Angel, let's go to the police," Arthur suggested.

"The police can't help me."

I saw the frustration written all over Arthur's face.

"I feel so helpless," Arthur said. "Angel, let me help you."

I had never experienced anything that dramatic. It had become more than a nightmare. Arthur picked up the roses, gathered up the black petals scattered all over the hallway floor, and threw them in the trash. Eric was totally losing it.

Where is his mind? This man is crazy and he's not afraid of anything.

"Angel, I don't want this guy to hurt you, so please let me help you," Arthur repeated.

Black roses were Eric's signature, and he was so elusive. It was as though he did not exist. That chapter seemed to have no ending. Wherever I went, he was there. I was running from a ghost-like figure.

I was experiencing a horrific time in my life, one that could literally destroy me. I had to believe my life would not end there. God had brought me too far to see me fall. I was no match for Eric Richards, a man totally out of control. Like a domino effect, Eric was going down and wanted to take someone with him: me.

For nine months he was able to cover his tracks very well. He knew exactly how to hide the truth. That man wore many faces and was able to mask the reality of who he really was. He hid behind a Bible to conceal the true identity of his soul.

The game Eric played was a dangerous one. That man played with fire to garner a thrilling rush, the power of control, and energy from the fear of those around him. For nine months I had been taken in; it took that long for him to show his true colors. I was completely off balance; everything about me was so unstable. I had become so unsure of myself.

"Angel, are you all right?" Arthur asked.

No words came to mind. I was numb, tired, and disgusted with the whole matter. I looked at the situation and my heart cried with deep emotion. Sadness overtook me and pierced my soul. I saw me falling.

How can this be?

I had traveled twenty-five hundred miles to make a new start. After all that effort, I was caught up in a cruel, demented web that seemed virtually impossible to escape.

"God, help me. I'm trapped and can't get out," I prayed.

I remembered months ago my life had begun to take shape. One wrong turn, one bad decision to follow my heart, and I lost footing. I slipped and fell hard into another horrific web. Every ounce of my being had fallen apart. I had gone over the edge.

"Arthur, I've got to get away. I don't want to stay here. He's going to kill me."

"Angel, he's not going to hurt you. I'm here."

Wrapped in Arthur's arms, I sobbed until every part of me hurt. I was confused and frightened; I shook like a leaf. My heart pounded as overwhelming fear took hold of me and ripped me apart. Arthur did his best to calm me down. He made me a glass of warm milk and tucked me in the bed like a baby.

"Sleep is what you need, angel. I love you. You're going to be all right," Arthur reassured me.

I kept running into dead ends as I lay in the bed. I had never felt that way before. I knew Eric fed off of my fear.

It must be a rush, some kind of high for him.

I wondered how many others he had done this to.

Where do I go? How far must I run to get away from this man?

Eric was totally incapable of reasoning.

God, I'm going to die, aren't I?

Everything I hoped for, loved, and tried to achieve had been lost. The world that had been taken away from me was truly gone. A dark, sullen shadow hovered over me and cast me down. It followed me wherever I went and lurked around every bend.

I had resolved I was going to die at the hands of a monster. Eric Richards was not going to stop until he killed me. I tried to hold on to my sanity as I ran around in circles, petrified out of my mind. Yet, I still prayed for a miracle. My emotions ran wild as I perceived death all around me.

I had entered a chapter of my life far worse than my experience with T. J. Masterson. I was dealing with someone incapable of reasoning. In those nine months, time had slipped through my fingers. So much of that time had been wasted on that crazy man.

My journals were filled with the expressions of my heart. The pen continued to describe the tears I shed. Never did I think my whole life was affected. Everything I held dear had to be put on hold.

As I lay in the quietness of the night, some of my thoughts were just a faint memory. Scattered ashes of days gone by. Grief overwhelmed me, and my thoughts opened the feelings of my heart.

CHAPTER 15

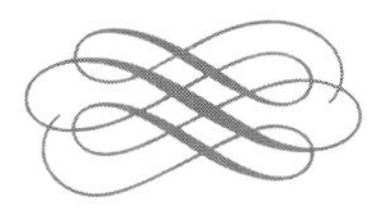

Thorns and Thistles

Ambiguous shadows of days gone by and bittersweet memories of earlier years of my life still came into play. Handwritten words expressed the feelings of my heart. My mother never bit her tongue or hesitated to let me know how much she did not love or want me. My birth was definitely not a timeless treasure, but more of grievous pain. Although my mother was there in body, mind, and soul, her heart was with my brothers.

I hated my life for such a long time, and as I sat in the midst of my horrific chapter, I was broken. My heart had been shattered and scrambled, and pieces of me had been lost and forgotten. I wondered where my life would end.

My eyes burned with tears, and my thoughts were clouded with the hurt I felt, yet I had a sense of hope because I knew if no one else loved me, God loved me.

What a big mess I've made of my life.

I had stubbed my toe so often I had lost count. As I shivered in total horror, I hung on as I prayed for my miracle. Somewhere I had strayed too far and lost myself; somewhere I made a wrong turn and got on a crooked path filled with absolute nothingness. It was a useless road that led absolutely nowhere. My dreams, aspirations, and expectations had died. Somehow I had made a complete mess of everything; subsequently, I ended up with Eric as my hideous nightmare.

Twenty-five hundred miles from where it all began, I might as well have been clear across the ocean. My mistakes and stupid decisions had thrown me into another dimension.

How could I have been so careless?

So absolutely oblivious to what was happening around me. I lived my life in the fast lane and gambled everything; it seemed as though I had failed. From my childhood until that chapter being written, I had built a wall around me to protect myself. Yet, I became my own worst enemy, instead of being cautious. I fell like a ton of bricks at the first sight of a good-looking man with a Bible.

My life was so uncertain. Blank lines on empty pages had no meaning or direction. Mistakes had caused me to drown in my tears.

I did not have to live that way; I did have choices. I did not have to dwell in the past. I did not have to let the past cripple me. I did not have to be the product of my mother's wrath, Uncle Jerry's madness, T. J.'s abusiveness, and I definitely did not have to be the target of Eric Richards' demented obsession.

Me, myself, and I had been bad enough, but *I* always seemed to make matters worse. I picked rotten apples from that same old, broken down, wooden barrel I had picked from for years.

Do I have a death wish? Do I enjoy pain? What's wrong with me? Am I that desperate? Is this how I value my life?

I kept jumping from the frying pan into the fire; somehow, I was stuck in that old, smelly barrel, in over my head in tears, time after time.

As the days had gotten longer and seasons changed, I saw the trees take on new life. Those tall, barren ones behind the old wooden shed flourished. The sparrows played hide and seek in the fullness of the tree leaves.

A new chapter waited to be written, stories waited to be told. My mind sprang forth new thoughts and ideas. My whole attitude had experienced a makeover. I got stronger as time passed. Ardent and passionate for life again, I was filled with enthusiasm and zeal to see what God had planned for me. That was why I did not quit.

It would have been nice if Eric Richards had fallen off the face of the earth or somehow disappeared. In reality, I knew that was not going to happen, so I continued to live my life until I got it right.

Back in the bus yard for another twelve-hour shift, I prayed that day would be a good one. I drove down Western Avenue and stayed busy. In fact, I did not have a layover. Halfway through my run, I spotted Eric's black Camaro parked by a fast food restaurant. Everything I had not wanted to feel, I felt. Anxiety had taken hold of me and my stomach was upset. As I drove up and down Western Avenue that day, there was no sign of that man anywhere.

Where's he hiding?

That night during my shift, I never knew when Eric would surface. Finally, my shift ended. I collected my things and quickly headed home. My life had become sheer madness—I always looked over my shoulder to see who lurked in dark shadows. Eric was like a harsh wind, I never knew when the storm approached. In the total chaos and utter confusion; I never knew where that man was or when Eric would show up.

Morning arrived, and I was running very late. I made a few stops before my shift started. Afterwards, I had to pick up some shirts at the cleaners for Arthur. What a beautiful day: the sun was bright and shining and the air was clear and crisp. I drove with my car windows down as my forehead rested against my propped forearm. I listened to some classic favorites on the radio. I was enjoying the day.

I made a left onto Washington Boulevard, and as I looked into my rearview mirror, Eric's Camaro was directly behind me. I drove down one street, up another street as I tried to lose him. I was lost in a virtual maze. Suddenly, I looked in my rearview mirror and Eric was gone. I continued on 4th Street; as I turned on Spring Street that black Camaro cut right in front of me and stopped.

"Get out of the car, Mary!" Eric shouted as he walked toward me. "Don't make me mad!"

Cars passed and I saw people walk by, but not a soul tried to help me.

"Get out, Mary!" he yelled as he pounded on my car window. "Get out now!"

I could not back my car up because I was trapped. I did not know what to do. In the middle of Spring Street, with all the traffic and confusion, no one even stopped or took notice of what was happening. It was as though Eric and I were invisible.

"Get out of the car, Mary!" he continued to shout as madness washed over his face.

"Stop, Eric, you're crazy . . . Leave me alone!"

I was stuck between a rock and a hard place. As Eric shouted and screamed, he went nuts. He was in my face and called me all sorts of names.

"Eric, you're insane," I shouted. "Somebody's going to call the police!"

Out of nowhere, sirens blasted and cop cars swarmed everywhere.

"Miss, are you all right?" one officer asked. "What's going on here?"

Eric stood against a patrol car as officers spoke to him. I quickly got out of my car.

"My ex-boyfriend is crazy, and he's harassing me! He follows me everywhere," I cried. "Please do something!"

One of the officers, who had been talking to Eric, came over to me.

"Miss, you'll have to go down to the station if you want to file a complaint," he said.

"What! This guy is nuts, but you can't stop him?"

"Calm down, Miss, it's going to be all right," the officer reassured me.

"Great. Another repeat of Caldwell Hills," I murmured to myself. "Does it ever stop?"

Eric pulled his car away, and then the cops pulled off. I got back into my car and headed down to the police station. It turned out to be a futile trip; once again nothing happened.

"Unless you can prove your complaint or physical abuse, I'm sorry, there's nothing we can do," the officer explained.

I did not say a word as I shook my head and walked down the steps disgusted, frustrated, and pissed off. I went to my car, but before I drove off, I lay my head on the steering wheel and sobbed uncontrollably.

I can't win for losing. I'm stuck, trapped, a walking target for Eric and his madness.

Running late, I rushed into the division, took my day sheet and run, and then got on my bus. The entire day I ran behind schedule. Around 4:00 pm my dispatcher called.

"Operator, I need you to pull a tripper for me; it's the Hollywood Park Race Track," he said.

Gosh, I thought I'd be done early, but I'll be out here until the early morning.

When I arrived at my layover, I called Arthur to leave him a message to tell him I would be home late. I made my last trip and headed toward Hollywood Park. The wait there seemed endless: 5:00 pm, 7:00 pm, and then it was closer to 8:30 pm when finally, I got a group of passengers ready to head back to Hollywood Boulevard.

Halfway back, sounds of thunder from afar rumbled and lightning was everywhere. The entire sky lit up like Fourth of July. It was scary out there, and the roads were slippery. The traffic was treacherous; all I could do was focus on my run. I maintained my composure and did not want fear to set in.

When I reached the stop, I called out, "Hollywood Boulevard!"

We had finally made it, and droplets of rain were falling—the storm had not reached there yet. I started to drive back up Western Avenue toward the freeway and headed back to the division. Suddenly, bright lights from an upcoming car approached me. As the car came closer, I carefully moved into the right lane. I thought the car wanted to pass me, but as I moved over, the car moved as well. It pulled directly behind me and its bright lights blinded me.

I can't see a thing!

I moved out of the car's path again. As I looked down, Eric was beside me. A cold and clammy feeling washed over me as beads of sweat rolled down my face. Eric blew his horn and motioned for me to pull over.

I tried to ignore him as I headed back to the transit division as fast as possible. He eased his car closer to the side of the bus, and it seemed he was trying to run me off the road.

"Lord, help me. Please, not here, not now!" I cried out.

I tried to use my radio, but I could not get through. The road was wet and slippery, and the rain came down hard. It was difficult to see. I did all I could not to have an accident.

The freeway seemed to be a never ending road of nothingness; not a soul was in sight. It looked deserted. Halfway through that madness, I saw red lights flash ahead, glaring bright lights that cut through the darkness. I knew if I saw the lights, Eric had seen them, too. Then, as quickly as he appeared, Eric disappeared.

I saw him get off the freeway and drive South. His car continued to move further away from me. I choked up with tears, my hands shook, and my heart pounded,

I quickly got off at the next exit near the division and looked for Eric at every corner and bend. At 2:15 am, I pulled into the division and signed off. Tired and weary, I headed out the door. After that, things got much worse. Eric Richards had played the invisible man. He taunted and stalked me to drive me crazy.

I was stuck between thorns and thistles, caught in a huge briar bush, and trapped and entangled with no way out. Eric came from the wrong side of the tracks; that man was out there. How I got caught up in his pool of filth, only God knows. It seemed I was going backwards instead of forward. I was in a freeze frame nailed to the wall.

From New Jersey to California I had traveled over twenty-five hundred miles of stretched out highway and crossed terrains. Instead of a new beginning, my life had become a continuation of years past. Journals noted heartaches and tears, pages filled with regrets and fears.

Instead of doing things my way, I decided to give God the reigns to my life and let Him work things out. I had not come that far to turn back. I had come too far to call defeat. Even though I had fallen between thorns and thistles, I was determined to survive.

Days passed and there was no sign of Eric anywhere: it was welcomed. However, I knew it was the calm before another storm. I thought I had run with the best and worst of them; I just knew I had it all together.

I had thought I was a good judge of character after my lesson with T. J. Masterson, but I was so very wrong. Eric Richards had completely fooled me. That crazy man pulled a switch on me. He had a double identity. Twenty-five hundred miles from my past, and I was still dodging bullets.

That entire week my run was hideous. I ran like crazy up and down the Hollywood Hills. One Friday night as I drove through the back hills of Park La Brea, that black Camaro was directly behind me.

Not here, not now.

Since I thought I knew the area well, I tried to lose him. So, I took the back roads through the mountains. I turned here and there, but as I made my left turn on Dry Canyon Cold Creek Road, I realized I had driven into a dead end.

What was I thinking? How was I supposed to lose him in this forty-foot bus!

At the bottom of the hill there was a small embankment with a riverbed was at its base. I was trapped and my radio was not working. I was in a very dangerous situation.

"Oh God!" I shouted in a panic. "Eric!"

I saw him approach the bus through my right side mirror.

"Mary, open this door, now!"

I realized Eric had a gun, and it was pointed at me. I was stuck in an isolated area and saw no one for miles as a crazy man banged on the door.

"Open the door, Mary, before I lose my patience!"

Suddenly, another vehicle approached us from behind. I was unable to see who it was because the vehicle headlights blinded me. A man in a dark black jacket got out and approached Eric. Fear took hold of me and in a panic I quickly shut off the bus engine and lights.

Who is that and why is he here?

Then, I quietly walked to the back of the bus to avoid being seen. I listened intently to find out what was going on.

"Man, are you crazy!" the man shouted. "You're losing your mind, man, not to mention being stupid . . . Give me the gun!"

That man knows Eric!

I slowly returned to the front of the bus and started the engine. I had decided I was not going to wait around any longer. I drove through the open field alongside the old warehouse. I was running for my life—I had run out of options.

Sweat rolled down my face, and I trembled all over. My heart pounded as I choked back tears. My entire being was harried, but I had to stay in control.

Left, right, where do I go? I'm lost.

I kept looking in my rearview mirror. I heard my heart pound as I went through that nightmare.

"Mary, wake up, wake up!" I told myself.

I could not wake up because what was happening was, in fact, very real.

Between thorns and thistles, the pricks of that nail-biting, horrific nightmare, my emotions ran wild. I could not allow my emotions to cripple me and wished I could pretend nothing was happening, but I had to maintain my sanity.

I had been there before—entrapped in corridors of my life as far back as my early childhood on Essex Avenue. How many chapters had I witnessed uncertainty and instability. Like that little girl in Mama's attic, at thirty-something I was wrapped in that same fear. Yet, I could not focus on the future unless I took my feet out of the past.

How tragic that one wrong turn, one bad move had landed me in the devil's hands. It seemed I was going down, but I refused to do so. I had fallen, but I was going to get back up.

I sensed more than ever—though tangled in another vicious web—God would help me. One day I was going to walk out of that horrific chapter of my life victoriously.

CHAPTER 16

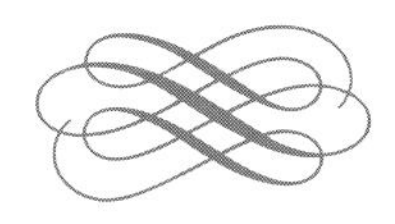

Mind Games

My entire life I had carelessly thrown my heart to the wolves, only to find I was trapped in the middle of a terrifying nightmare, unsure if I would come out alive. Not in my wildest imagination did I ever suspect Eric Richards was another predator. Nine months since that Sunday morning when I met that man, a beautiful dream turned deadly. It had almost taken my life and I could not seem to wake up.

My entire life had dangled by a thin thread. I was too close to the edge and it was just a matter of time before I fell flat on my face again.

I could not run away forever; that would mean defeat. That man could not win; I had to win in the end. Half out of my mind with fear, I had learned a lot from T. J. Masterson.

"It's not over until it's over," he warned me.

Young and vulnerable, I allowed T. J. to take control of my life. As payback, T. J. tried to annihilate me.

No, absolutely not! I'm not running away again! That's not the answer!

I knew if I continued to run, I would be running forever. I was tired. From one chapter to the next, I had been torn down by so many people. Somehow, they pushed me right out of the box.

Twenty-five hundred miles from where it all started, and I continued to run for my life from a vicious cycle of contempt and deceit.

Those chapters had been left behind. Those bridges I had already crossed. I wondered if I would ever be able to cross back over those dormant pathways to recover all that was taken from me.

For the next few months I stayed on the Broadway line, The 45 came out of a different division. I did all I could to get rid of that man, but no matter how hard I tried, Eric always found me. I truly did not know what it would take to shake Eric off, but I knew what I had to do. I knew running from Eric Richards would not make him go away; it only made him stronger.

The days got colder, and the night skies set in much earlier. Many evenings, I would drive down Broadway and Temple Street into the early morning hours and waited for bus connections to arrive. Downtown Los Angeles was like a ghost town. Every time I drove into my layover, I made sure I sat under the huge lights of Union Station, so I was able to see more clearly when anyone approached my bus.

One particular stormy night, I was at the layover without a soul in sight. The night sky was threatening, and I perceived death had walked over my grave. My thoughts ran wild as I waited for Eric to show up. I had no idea when that monster would strike.

As I sat at Union Station, I heard the rain come down on the roof of the bus. It rained so bad outside that visibility was almost at zero. Earlier that day, my bus gave me problems, so on my second trip I went back to the transit division for a bus change.

When I arrived at the Southgate division, I had a small break, so I bought a bag of chips and a can of soda, and sat in the driver's room to relax. Getting a new bus seemed to take forever; obviously, there was no bus available. So, until they called me, I chilled out and enjoyed the calmness.

"Operator, your bus is ready!" the clerk announced over the loud speaker.

I had caught my second wind, so I picked up my paperwork, and I walked out to the yard to pick up the bus. It rained so badly, I was saturated. I remember as a child I played a silly game. I would run through the raindrops down Chapel Street and up the hill to Essex Avenue, yet no matter how hard I ran, by the time I arrived home I was soaked.

I remember those beautiful, simpler days of my life with steaming hot chocolate filled with tiny marshmallows, topped with mounds of whipped cream. I sat at the center of the kitchen table where Mama's homemade cornbread, tubs of homemade apple butter, and lots of baked cookies were. My mother did a little bit of everything, but her specialties were honed from the hours she spent in the kitchen.

I also remember baskets of freshly picked Granny Smith apples, sweet D'Anjou pears, and all sorts of berries picked and put into jars that sat in front of the pantry door while pots of homemade apple cider simmered atop the stove. Even as I experienced my latest nightmare, I cherished those precious memories. My heart opened up as those memories gave me sweet solace and peace. It was something that soothed my aching heart, even through my brokenness.

I pulled my bus out of the yard, but before I made my turn I called the dispatcher to get back on time. It was a cold, damp, rainy night; the weather was completely disgusting. I felt wet and icky, even my uniform did not smell fresh anymore.

It was a night that seemed to keep everyone out of the rain. I drove up and down the boulevard for hours. The bus remained empty all the way. All I had to do was keep from Broadway, so I hummed a few tunes from the 1960s and laughed at myself while I sang.

It could be quite lonesome out there, especially when all I saw for miles were vehicle lights running up and down the street while horns blew and dogs barked.

At least there's life somewhere out here besides me.

Time moved slowly. Even my watch looked like it stopped. So, whenever I arrived at a layover, I walked around to avoid falling asleep. The streets were unusually empty, and not too many people were out in the rain.

When I made a left turn to head down by the old brewery, I turned my head, and then looked up: Eric was standing behind me.

"Well, Mary, why are you avoiding me?" he asked in a soft whisper.

I was petrified and taken aback. I was shocked at the sight of him.

How did he get on my bus?

"Mary, you look surprised to see me. You look as white as a ghost. Are you afraid of me?" he asked calmly.

I could not respond; I was speechless and terrified. My throat was parched, and I was as cold as ice. I knew that was the end of me. It was so dark that night, and all the lights lit on the bus were courtesy lamps. Eric being dressed all in black made it harder for anyone to see him.

A horrible fear took over my entire being. Trapped in that fear, I remembered Mat's words: *Mary, he feeds off of your fear.*

I was at the mercy of that madman.

"Eric, please. You're sick, so don't do anything you'll regret," I pleaded.

"Shut up, Mary. If I want to kill you, I'll kill you and you can't stop me!" he shouted.

I'm truly a sitting duck!

"Stop the bus, Mary! Pull over now!"

I was stuck between my seat and the steering wheel. There was not a thing I could do, but pull over and stop. Eric really looked bad; he was not the man I remembered. Whatever happened to him, it showed all over. He could no longer hide it.

"Why, Eric, why are you doing this?"

"What am I doing? I'm doing nothing," he said calmly.

"Eric, please. Leave me alone; I haven't done anything to you," I reasoned.

As I looked at him, I saw a change take place that truly scared me. I was not at all sure if I should mention his brother or not. I did not want to cause a negative chain reaction, so I kept quiet about that.

"You smell pretty, Mary. You always do. I love you, why can't you love me?" he asked as tears filled his eyes.

For the very first time, in a long time, I saw some human emotion come from him. I had never seen Eric cry. As he moved from behind me and went down the stairwell, those tears turned into rage.

Eric walked back up the bus steps and warned, "Don't make me hit you, Mary . . . Don't make me kill you!"

I did not say a word. I sat and stared down at him. I watched his expressions change.

"Mary, what happened? I love you. You're not getting away with this!"

My heart pounded like it was going to explode. I was so scared the look on his face alone frightened me. His wide, glossy, dark eyes had such a dead look. He was so angry his body language showed it.

Suddenly, he started talking to himself. He walked up and down the bus aisle and punched his fist against the palm of the other hand.

"She's not getting away with this, she's not," he ranted.

"Operator where are you?" the dispatcher asked over the radio. "Come in please."

I was very late returning to the bus yard, and they were looking for me. As I reached to answer the call, Eric came from behind and yanked the radio handset out of my hand and hung it up.

"Open this door, Mary! You haven't seen the last of me!"

He reached over me and pushed the metal lever to open the door.

"I'll be back. I promise you, Mary, I will!"

I pulled into my layover and shook like a leaf. There were people everywhere. I was so beside myself I did not know what to do or say, or how to act.

Should I call in sick, or continue my run?

I knew I had very little choice in the matter since many of the drivers had already called in sick. Being the last bus out, I knew I would be stuck there, so I continued my run and when I arrived at Broadway and Aliso Street, Eric's black Camaro was parked across the street down by the cleaners.

That guy was playing mind games; he knew he would not get caught, so he kept taunting me with his madness. I sat for a while, and then suddenly the lights of the Camaro came on. He flashed his high beams in my face. It was time for me to leave and that entire night, Eric drove up and down Broadway directly behind the bus.

Around 1:45 am, I finished my run. As I pulled away from my last stop, Eric was gone. When I arrived at the division, Fish, one of the clerks, called me over to the front desk.

He said, "Mary, some guy left these for you."

He handed me black roses tied in black satin ribbons wrapped in clear plastic.

"I never saw black roses. Pretty sick, don't you think?" Fish asked.

What could I say? There was not much to say. I did not have an answer. I had reached a point where I did not care anymore. I realized I was fighting a losing battle. Kill me; kill me not—whatever game Eric had been playing was driving me crazy. Whatever he had planned to do, I wished he would get it over with.

Eric had lost it. I was so mad I wanted to rip Eric apart. Everyone wanted to help me, but Eric was so far beyond anyone's imagination I feared for their lives. I did not know what to do. All I had to show for his torment were those hideous black roses. Not even the police could help me.

I stayed on guard and looked before I leaped. I became aware of my surroundings and tried to stay ahead of Eric's madness, but every attempt was fruitless. Still, I kept my eyes wide open. Even Arthur started to ride my bus on his days off. I was trapped and knew it.

"He's crazy," Rosie said.

"Mary, he's gonna hurt you," Jane cried.

Arthur, Bill, and Earl wanted to get involved. They thought talking to him would make a difference, but Eric was so crazed, I did not want anyone hurt.

What am I going to do?

I could not dig a hole and bury myself. I could not stop living, so I lived one day at a time and prayed for a miracle.

"Angel, we can move away. I can work from anywhere," Arthur offered.

"No, Arthur," I replied. "I can't run forever."

Bless that man's heart, but I had to deal my dilemma head on. After that night, things seemed to quiet down, and Eric disappeared for a while. However, after all the hell that man had put me through, I was not naïve enough to think he had simply walked off into the sunset and would leave me alone.

I took some time off from work. Many of those nights, Arthur and I sat out back and enjoyed the beautiful evenings. At times, Grandma Blanche would join us. One Saturday night as Arthur was grilling, he and I shared a lot about our past.

Arthur had lived a full life: from the Marines to his band, The Lost Souls. He had logged many hours playing basketball and driving buses up and down the boulevard. Arthur truly had no regrets.

On the other hand, I came from the 1960s era of fringe vests and bell bottom jeans. I spent hours in Greenwich Village, listening to poetry and recitals. On Saturday mornings, I wore long floral dresses and sang tunes of guitar players in Miller's Pond by the big fir trees.

Arthur and I were walking scrapbooks filled with beautiful memories and stories of days gone by. Together, we shared memories. With all the twists and turns that were happening, those treasured moments were welcomed.

Getting involved with Eric was definitely one of my biggest mistakes.

How did I get so strung up on a man who had a mental problem?

Eric Richards was a total nightmare, who got a rush from terrorizing me. That entire chapter had become a complete disaster. Stopping him seemed hopeless. I never know what to expect and never knew what that man was going to do next. He ran the show and kept me living on the edge.

Christmas was approaching, and I started to make plans for the season. I did a little bit of everything. I remember the Christmases back on Essex Avenue when my mother cooked for days. She made her homemade goodies and her specialty delights. I remember staying glued to the pantry, which was where she stacked all her baked pies and cookies to cool them off and keep them away from Daddy and me.

What a beautiful time of year that was for us. Red valor drapes were tied back with thick gold fringes. Evergreens twined with grapes and fruits, and nuts and figs were mounted on our mantels. A huge Douglas fir about twelve feet tall was dressed with gorgeous gold bulbs, huge white snowflakes dangled between the silver ice sickles and the multi-colored teardrops, and comfortable firesides burned while Christmas carols played. Those Christmases were treasured moments in my life.

Arthur loved the same things I loved, which made all the difference in the world to me. It made it easier for me to move forward with my life. I stayed busy putting up lights, wreaths, and all sorts of Christmas decorations. One afternoon as I listened to Christmas music, I heard someone's footsteps in the hall. I quickly walked over to the door and looked through the peephole, but I saw nothing.

I heard the footsteps again, and when I looked through the peephole a second time, Eric's eyes met mine. He stood in the hallway and looked back at me. I ran to the telephone to call the police. No sooner had I dialed the number and Eric ran down the hall, out the courtyard to the street where his Camaro was parked, and drove away.

I sobbed like a baby, and then fell on my knees and prayed.

"Nothing is stopping him, Lord. Help me please," I cried as Grandma Blanche comforted me.

Eric showed no fear. He waited outside the apartment, down at the division, and in crowds at bus stops, yet no one seemed to see him, except me. The only proof I had were those black roses he left behind.

Eric was familiar with the game he played. I was sure I was not the first woman he had stalked. Like a spider weaving a web, Eric's cunning and slick personality trapped his victims. When he became comfortable, he finally revealed his ugly self.

What a web he has weaved. He won't let me go.

He was determined to control me. He was clearly obsessed and the game he played was so dangerous, I was truly afraid he was going to win.

The holiday was drawing near, but I was trying to deal with the circumstances around me. There were days when the Christmas spirit was silent, and I felt nothing. Yet, there were days when it was very much alive with singing Christmas carols by the fireside.

"God, please help me. I'm worn out," I prayed.

I was at my wit's end. My thoughts and emotions were so out of sorts. I stayed in a state of confusion and tears because I was unsure from one day to the next when Eric would show his face. I lived on an emotional rollercoaster headed toward disaster.

I went back to work and was stuck on the Santa Fe Avenue bus line. Many nights I drove clear across the tracks to the suburban city of Norwalk. Eric showed his face in crowds of passengers. At times, he would not even board the bus; he would stand in the midst of the passengers and stare at me with those cold stone eyes.

No words could begin to describe how dreadfully scared I was; my stomach stayed in knots. There were many days I was too sick to go to work, but I knew I had to go on. Somehow, I had to face my giant: one of my greatest fears. It was a situation of which I had no control that took control of my mind, body, and soul. I feared it would finally take me under.

Running from Eric Richards was not the answer. It had been proven to be fruitless when I went up North and he followed and found me.

Days passed, and I decided to call back home, but the telephone had been disconnected. All sorts of crazy thoughts ran through my mind. I did not know what had happened. I wrote letters, but there were no answers as usual. Twenty-five hundred miles way, I was unable to get a reply from my family. That alone was enough to blow my mind.

Something was wrong, but I did not know what to do. I was buried under the rubble and ashes of my shattered life, which became much harder to get from under. My intentions were to bring my family to live with me. I prayed feverishly day and night as I worked toward my goal.

That Trailways bus had pulled out of Penn Station a year and a half ago and was a springboard for a better future. I had cried countless tears of uncertainty about where my journey would take me. I came to California on a wing and a prayer. I had placed my faith in God, believing He would direct me. I was no closer to reconnecting with my little family than I had been when I left New Jersey.

I had no clue about the outcome of that chapter. I knew God had not brought me as far as He had to see me fall, so I kept going.

From Darkness to Dawn[4] was written from the heart, every bit of my emotions had been poured out on the pages of that book. All those crazy feelings were put on display chapter after chapter as heartfelt life-changing events were recounted. Experiences I had drawn strength from, even as they unfolded, were survived because my God was with me. He never left my side.

Eric's mind games were intended to drive me over the edge. T. J. Masterson tried that same tactic and failed. Eric Thomas Richards, a man far worse than T. J. Masterson could ever be, had consumed my life. I was falling apart at the seams and splitting in every direction, yet I would not call defeat. Somehow, someway one of us was going to cave in—either him or me.

I got to a point where fear meant nothing. Somehow, somewhere inner strength surfaced and I began to fight back. Something inside went off and, suddenly, enough was enough. Eric Thomas Richards had become a thorn in my side. If I failed to fight back, that man was destined to kill me.

The week of Christmas arrived, and Arthur had to work late shifts. One night Grandma Blanche had gone Christmas shopping with Rosie and I did not want to be alone. So, I went to church

---

4 Ibid.

and attended Bible study. I drove down to Crenshaw Boulevard to Hyde Park, and as I drove along, a car came up behind me with its high beams on. The glare blinded my eyes.

I did not stop, but kept driving. I quickly made a right on Van Ness Avenue. As I turned, those lights disappeared. Around 9:30 pm I headed back home. I was on my p's and q's as Eric had me on a short leash; at least he thought he did.

That man was a manipulator, conniver, and unpredictable. His destructive behavior and bad temper turned any situation into a living hell.

Every day was a challenge as he had become the hunter and I had become the prey. In New Jersey I had places to hide out, but in California I had no place to hide. Wherever I went, Eric found me. I was on Eric's stumping grounds where he knew how to disappear. In fact, he did a good job to keep from being found.

When I arrived home, I saw Eric's black Camaro across the street from the apartment complex. The night sounds filled the air: dogs barked, sirens blared, and gunshots rang out from afar. Eric waited and lurked in night shadows—I was helplessly visible.

I quickly walked to the apartment. The brown doormat was covered with black roses. Next to them were two enormous, white stone candlestick holders with black candles inside them. Also, an open note read: Rest in Peace. I quickly unlocked the door and rushed inside to call the police.

Everywhere I went, Eric's black roses followed me. Black roses symbolized death. I thought I had already been to hell, but hell had no fury like the madness of Eric Richards.

Where do I go from here? Where do I run and hide?

It seemed I was in a darkened forest, surrounded by death summons. The enemy had tried his best through Eric to destroy me. The devil tried to take every part of me and make me give up, but as long as the Lord was beside me, I continued to fight for my life.

I cannot begin to understand what that man was thinking. Everyone knew what the color black meant: death was the message Eric had tried to convey. It was clearly a distinctive connection to his distorted, twisted, evil side. He had, however, put a twist on his already unusual behavior when he used a specific symbol to represent the feelings of his hear.

Eric was a man who loved to terrorize, punish, and destroy. A sadist, he loved sick humor. A twist of irony: he was a Bible-toting man, who loved the book of John, yet he turned out to be a wolf in sheep's clothing. I truly believed I was fighting the devil.

I had walked through many seasons in life. Chapters had been written, and stories had been told. I stayed prayerful for my miracle because I so badly wanted peace and to be free from those chains that kept me down. I made a pot of tea and honey, and then sat by the fire and enjoyed the rest of the evening.

A thin line between life and death, and love and hate existed. It did not take much to turn someone's world upside down. Eric Richards was very good at that; he thrived on making other people miserable. Eric was destroyed and broken, and brought with him an unspeakable series of events.

He weaved a web with threads of anger, frustration, bitterness, and hatefulness. Then he ties them with a vengeful heart. He lay in wait to trap his victims to make them pay for what he had gone through.

I had already experienced many unthinkable brushes with death over the years. The years of T. J. and me could have taken me out, journals were filled describing Uncle Jerry's madness, and many gruesome nights I had been at the mercy of his demented, twisted world. Diaries stacked with pages written with agonizing tears reflected on why Mama did not love me, and the brutality of her anger and fear toward me.

I examined my heart and prayed I to not become bitter and hateful like them.

How did I walk through those valleys of the shadow of death, many years in the open, hot, dry desert, and not turn sour?

I prayed not to become vengeful. I did not want to lash out and impose the feelings of my heart on others. God was truly with me, and because of His unfailing love, I was able to go on in spite of the hell I had lived through.

Death had taken center stage. Nothing, but the blackness of ominous, threatening, and eerie feelings surrounded me. True, I did not know the ending of that story. I still tripped over my feet.

Whatever Eric Thomas Richards was going to do, whatever message of death he tried to convey, whatever he tried to achieve, I knew unless God was ready for me, death would not take me. Eric Richards would not win.

CHAPTER 17

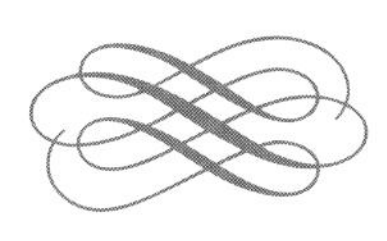

Verdes Cliffs

I had a lot of unfinished business to complete, and until I got things right, I believed the Lord had His hands on me. God worked behind the scenes, so I thought positively. Whatever the outcome of that chapter may have been, I had to believe God was in control.

I was worn out, and my nerves were shot. With Eric on my tail, my whole world was turned upside down. Everything about my life was so incomplete. With Eric Richards inserted in my life, my whole world I was topsy-turvy.

Life had been a mystery, which made it difficult to figure out the thoughts and intent of a person's heart. We lived in a real world and life was much too short to worry about what cannot be controlled.

God, am I going to die? Eric Richards isn't going to stop. He keeps terrorizing me and I'm standing on the brink of insanity.

A whole new chapter was about to begin—the chapter of Arthur and me. The question remained: will I be able to write that chapter in time? I was so close, yet so far. The Lord had not allowed me to come twenty-five hundred miles to die. I left New Jersey on a wing and a prayer. I stood on my faith, and through it all, I was alive to talk about it.

I learned a lot through those seasons of my life; my mistakes had been my greatest teacher. The school of hard knocks taught me well and built my character. Thank God I had become resilient, confident, and strong. Without a shadow of a doubt God had carried me—that was the faith I stood on. I believed in my heart God would finish what He started.

The days moved on, and a brand new year had begun. On Valentine's Day 1985, Arthur proposed to me. I never forgot that moment. It was about 1:35 am, and I had finished my shift. Arthur was supposed to pick me up, so I waited in the driver's room for quite a while. I even tried to call him, but there was no answer. It must have been about 2:05 am when Maggie and I left the division and headed up 54th Street to catch the Line 40 bus.

"Come on, Mary, you don't have to take the bus," Maggie said. "I'll take you home."

"Thank you," I replied.

We drove up 54th Street. Just before we reached Crenshaw Boulevard, Arthur's yellow van zipped around the corner. He was headed toward the division.

"Mary, there's Arthur!" Maggie exclaimed.

"Don't stop, Maggie, keep going."

I was upset with Arthur. For the past few days he had been in his own world. I did not know exactly what was wrong with him; that scared me. I knew that episode with Eric was a bit much, but up until then, Arthur seemed to be all right with it. Yet, because of the changes that had taken place, I knew something was wrong. So, I put my guard up and started to withdraw.

My thoughts ran wild; I did not know what to do.

"Mary, I'm stopping. I don't care what you say, Arthur loves you!" she insisted. "You must stop thinking so negatively!"

Maggie stopped the car. As she pulled over to the curb Arthur's yellow van stopped, too. Suddenly, the van door opened and Arthur ran over to her car in black and white polka dot pajamas with no shoes on his feet. His hair was uncombed.

He shouted at the top of his lungs, "Angel, I love you! Will you marry me?"

I laughed so hard. I could not believe what I saw. In the middle of 54th Street, at 2:30 am, the love of my life had proposed to me.

"Yes, I'll marry you, Arthur Adams," I shouted back. "I love you, too!"

"I'm so sorry for not picking you up. I overslept. I woke up out of my sleep saying, 'I love you, angel' over and over," Arthur said.

What a morning. In my wildest imagination, never had I ever dreamed something like that would ever happen to me. It was, a moment in time I always cherished. Arthur and I made plans for our wedding. Even the guest list was carefully worked out.

I was so excited I could not think of anything else. Even at work my mind was on Arthur. For days after that, I stayed busy. I was on the extra board, so I drove different lines. It was a big relief because I thought Eric would not keep up with my schedule. I was on standby for a while, but I did not mind because the flexibility gave me a chance to plan our wedding.

During the time my mind had a chance to clear negative thoughts manifested by Eric's madness. For a change, I felt a little more relaxed.

Arthur and I made an awesome couple; we were good together. We loved to dance and listen to music. In fact, many a night Arthur would serenade me on the piano and sang the oldies, but goodies. In the short time Arthur and I had been together, we had been through a lot. Because of that, the two of us had grown closer.

My entire life I had dreamed of a love like the one we shared. My dream had come true. Arthur and I did so much together: he loved what I loved; he even shared my love for animals. I could literally sit for hours and write in my journal, page after page filled with the love the two of us had.

Life is so strange: I had to travel twenty-five hundred miles to find the love of my life. God's design for life is so magnificent. He took my blank canvas and painted a beautiful watercolor picture perfectly designed for my life. I looked at my portrait of His love and I was ever so grateful for the masterpiece He created.

Arthur and I truly appreciated life. Many nights we drove to Palos Verdes Cliffs to watch the beautiful ocean waves as they crashed against the huge rocks below us. We listened to the sounds that came from their shear force. I was ecstatic, and although I was terrorized by Eric, the love I received from Arthur made all the difference in the world.

With everything going on around me, my job became more demanding. I stayed on the extra board for quite some time. One Friday night, after being on standby for five hours, the clerk let me go. I had plans that evening: a candlelight dinner for two in front of a warm, cozy fire; chocolate-covered strawberries; and bubbly champagne. To really set the evening off, I played some old 1960s classics.

I called home before I left the division. Arthur had not returned home yet. He and Grandma Blanche had not come back home from Oakland. He had taken her there because she had to settle some personal affairs.

I regretted Grandma Blanche had been exposed to that chapter in my life, but her presence during that time was invaluable. I knew she was confused, but she never asked questions. She simply showered me with unconditional love, comfort, and reassurance that God was in control.

I had some time to kill, so I drove up Crenshaw Boulevard to Torrance to see if Rosie and Bill had returned from their trip. It was about 9:45 pm, and while I waited for a light to change on Artesia Boulevard, my car stalled. I realized I was out of gas.

I put my hazard lights on and started to look for a gas station. I finally found one and purchased some gas. Then, I quickly walked back to my car. On my way back at around 11:30 pm, I heard thunder. Shortly thereafter, lightning lit up the sky.

I put the gas I had purchased into the gas tank and drove off, but then my car stalled once more. Rain poured down in buckets as I sat there. Time passed and when I looked at my watch, it read midnight. Darkness was all around me as I watched puddles form and tiny droplets of rain swirl around in circles as it hit the pavement.

I tried to restart my car, and it started. So, I continued to drive up Crenshaw Boulevard to the Pacific Coast Highway. As I made a left turn, Eric's black Camaro cut directly in front of me.

"Oh, God, no!" I cried. "This can't be!"

My car was stuck and could not be moved because Eric's car blocked me. I made several attempts to put may car into reverse; however, I shook like a leaf. I eventually flooded the engine.

"Mary, Mary, Mary, funny meeting you here. Where are you going?"

He stood beside my car and tapped on my window. He seemed spaced out as rain continued to pour and saturate him from head to toe. He repeatedly called my name.

"Eric, go away, I have to go . . . Move!" I insisted.

"Go, I'm not going anywhere, but you are."

Life fades like leaves on a cold, winter day when they fall from the branches of barren trees. They are tossed to and fro by the swiftness of a winter breeze. Likewise, my life hung in the balance like a leaf in the hands of a monster. It was out of control and being whisked away.

I looked straight ahead and did not want eye-to-eye contact. In that downpour, Eric stood and banged on the window, shouting my name.

"Open the door, Mary, don't make me bust the window!" he warned.

Suddenly, a huge bolt of lightning struck. It was as though the heavens had opened to illuminate the sky. Moments later, the loud sound of thunder rumbled. Eric stood in the pouring rain and looked at the lightning strikes. Suddenly, Eric walked away, got into his car, and left.

I was gasped for air and cried so hard I thought I was going to fall apart. I sat there for a while and caught my second wind, and then I drove off.

"God, those high beams are blinding me," I moaned. "Oh, no, it's him again!"

Eric rode directly behind me and tried to push me off the road. I drove faster, but he stayed right on my tailgate, tapping my bumper to ram my car out of control. The faster I drove, the faster he drove as he blinked his high beams incessantly.

I drove so fast, I missed the on ramp to the freeway. I drove on to 109th Street toward Crenshaw Boulevard. Suddenly, Eric passed my car and cut me off again. He jumped out of his car and walked over to mine with a metal crowbar in his hand.

"Stop, Eric, you're sick!"

He kept coming closer, and just as he reached my car I put it in reverse and backed up. Then, I drove away. My heart pounded, and it was hard for me to catch my breath. I looked ahead and saw blinking lights for a detour—the road ahead was closed.

The gas gauge did not look too good: I had to find another gas station. The rain continued to pour in buckets with cloud bursts everywhere. Visibility was terrible, and I barely saw the street lights ahead. I finally spotted a mini-mart and drove into the parking lot. The sign on the door read: closed.

This can't be happening! Dear God, help me!

When I got ready to pull back out, I saw a telephone booth by the restroom. I got out of the car and ran to it, all the while looking around for Eric. Once inside, I fumbled in my purse for some change.

Suddenly, I heard a loud bang on the glass.

"Mary, do you really think you can get away from me?"

He continued to bang on the glass; I thought it was going to break. Then, he took out a gun from his pocket and continued to bang on the glass door.

I'm trapped. He has me. I'm dead.

The rain continued to come down hard. Tears fell from my eyes and I felt faint.

"Get out, Mary, get out now!" Eric shouted. "And don't make me kill you!"

Without warning, he broke the glass and pushed open the door. He grabbed my arm and dragged me to his car.

"Walk, Mary . . . Move!"

The gun was pointed at the side of my head. That cold metal against my temple was a horrible feeling. My heart beat so fast, and I was cold and clammy. Sweat rolled down my face. He opened his car door, pushed me in, and ran around the car to get in, too. I tried to get away, but he was too fast for me.

"Don't make me kill you, Mary!"

I was scared out of my mind and death could not come fast enough. I welcomed death rather than to be terrorized by that monster.

"Well, Mary, I don't know what to say. I loved you. Why did you make a fool of me?"

"Eric, please don't hurt me," I whimpered.

I saw the gun pointed directly at me.

"Why, Eric, why? What have I done to you?"

"Mary, I love you and can give you the world, so why can't you love me?" he asked. "Turn around. Look at what I brought you . . . Look, look!"

Dozens of black roses tied with black satin ribbons lay in the backseat. Tears rolled down my face; I knew I was going to die. I stared at the rain as it pounded against the windshield. I was tired of running and no longer cared what happened. Whatever that man had planned to do, only God could stop him. Eric drove up one street and down another; I did not recognize where we were.

We must have driven for what seemed forever. Suddenly, he turned onto a winding road and the car started to climb a steep hill.

God, where are we?

Eric was so quiet; not a sound came from him. It was as though he was not there. Then, I heard the ocean sounds. Suddenly, he made a sharp turn onto a narrow roadway. The ocean sounds got louder, and I heard waves crash against the rocks.

Oh, no, it's the Verdes Cliffs!

He drove onto a dirt road, and then he made a sharp left turn onto Crescent Peaks. Then, he stopped the car.

"Mary, I know you always loved the ocean. Come, let's sit out on the rocks and watch the tide come in," Eric said calmly.

His temperament changed—Eric went from a Dr. Jekyll to Mr. Hyde. The rain kept coming down so hard I could not see very far. He got out of the car and walked over to my side.

"Mary, come, let's enjoy the night."

He took my arm, helped me out of the car, and walked me up the cliff. It was a scary climb; I could not see where I was walking. I heard the ocean sounds as waves crashed against the rocks. I stumbled as we continued to climb and tried not to fall.

We climbed up the cliff. He used his right hand to pull me up. The slopes were very slippery and I could not keep my footing. We finally reached the top of Verdes Cliff.

"Look, Mary, isn't it beautiful?"

I could not speak or think. Nothing, but fear surrounded me. Then, Eric seemed to suddenly change. His eyes had a stone cold gaze; absolute nothingness.

"Eric, what's wrong? Say something."

Out of him came another voice, a harsh, ugly voice. I was trapped. Where I stood, the drop was extremely steep. I was scared and did not know how to get down off the cliff. The ocean raged and roared, and thunder and lightning were everywhere. I was too terrified to move—I stood between the fury force of two hostile elements, both of which were harmful and deadly.

My eyes blinked rapidly as I tried to keep the heavy rain from getting into them. The saltwater mist and the pounding rain made it hard for me to keep from slipping.

"Mary, you made a fool of me! Do you think you can get away with this?" Eric shouted; his voice was deep and harsh.

I stood in complete fear for my life; I was at the mercy of a madman. My life flashed before me like I was flipping through pages of a chapter book. I saw so much of what used to be.

What I wanted to work out had not; once again, I had failed. My life hung by a thin thread; the chapters may have ended in that instance. The world I left behind may no longer exist.

I travelled this far just to die?

"God, help me. You're the only one who can help me now. Please don't allow my life to end here, don't let my life to have been lived in vain," I cried.

I knew the Lord had taken me off of the streets of Los Angeles—I had not died in the gutter like a lost soul. He rescued me from the hands of a madman. He protected me from a demented old man and comforted me. He showed me love when my mother did not.

As I stood on Verdes Cliff, in crippling fear, Life seemed to drain from me; yet, I knew no matter what, God was still with me.

"Lord, help me. Lord, please help me," I cried.

It seemed an eternity as I stood there; time seemed to have stood still. Thunder, lightning, and the surge of waves crashing against the rocks—the ocean current was powerful. I saw the water slush back and forth with extreme force. The white caps of the waves were gigantic.

I stood on a threshold between life and death and realized my life may come to a close. There was no way to stop it. Saturated from head to toe, I truly faced the devil on that cliff.

"Mary, I love you!" Eric cried out.

Eric sobbed uncontrollably as he stood in front of me. He was a very sick and troubled man.

"Mary, I love you. God knows how much I love you," Eric repeated.

A tug of war ensued right before my eyes: I saw a man wrestle with two personalities on top of that jagged cliff. I had been through so much in life, chapters filled with unbelievable stories.

Now this?

I was totally freaked out by the ocean sounds crashing beneath me. Suddenly, it was quiet. Eric sat down on the rocks with his knees to his chest and his hands clasped together. He was crying. I stood there as the rain poured down on us, the thunder roared, and the lightning lit the sky. I had no idea if I was going to live or die.

As I watched Eric, great sadness entered my heart. Even in the midst of fear, I felt pity for the man. In some small way, my fears seemed to vanish. Tears rolled down my face, yet not for me, but for Eric. A deep sympathy washed over me, as I wondered what had happened to that man to cause his personality to split.

The man I had met nine months ago—a strong pillar in the church—was far different from the man I saw in front of me. I guess Eric was not as fortunate as me in the fact he did not make it completely out of his past. The poor guy was trapped in a vicious web I had been so fortunate to escape.

I remember Dr. Conner, my old hometown physician, once said, "Mary, if you don't get out now, and leave the past in the past, you'll be trapped in it forever."

I did not know exactly what he meant back then, but whenever I reached the point where I felt broken, I remembered Dr. Conner's words of wisdom. Thank God, He gave me the strength to close those chapters of my life, In doing so I was able to move on.

Suddenly, Eric turned and looked at me.

"Mary, I love you. I'll never hurt you, so don't be afraid."

I knew at that point I was able to reason with him.

"Eric, please, let's go. I don't want to be up here," I suggested.

I watched him carefully, as I did not know how he would respond. The sky continued to light up as the thunder rolled everywhere. It got colder, and we were soaked.

Suddenly, Eric got up, walked over to me, and grabbed my arm. He led me down the cliff, and then we got back into his car and left the area. We rode in silence; not a word was spoken between us. I tried to regroup, catch my breath, and slow my thoughts down. When we reached my car, he stopped his car.

"Mary, I'm sorry. Truly, I am," Eric said.

There were no words to express how I felt in that moment. I looked at him, turned to open the car door, and left. I got into my car and quickly drove off before something else happened. That was one of the darkest hours of my life—my midnight hour. It was a thin line between life and death.

Where do I go from here? I don't want to run anymore.

I stood between two worlds: one I tried to hold onto and the other I wished would let me go. Eric Thomas Richards remained out there somewhere—a very sick and troubled man, who carried his past around with him.

Thoughts like those, and so much more, grasped my heart. Bittersweet fragments of the seasons of my life still brought tears to my eyes. Flipping through the seasons of my life still brought tears to my eyes. The pages of those chapters, coupled up with chapters of Eric and me, were engraved in my mind. I was not sure of anything anymore.

I was torn and remained stuck between where I wanted to be and where life had me. I wanted so much to move forward, but with that thorn in my side, I was crippled, paralyzed, and could not move on. Until that chapter of Eric and me came to an end, I could not move forward.

A part of me was scared and feared the inevitable. There was nothing normal about Eric. Three days from nowhere, and I could not seem to find a way out of that horrible period. I had thought so much about it my brain was overloaded. The lack of sleep caused my eyes to burn. That nightmare took a major toll on me. God bless Arthur, he was there for me.

Days had passed since that night, and I was still wound up. I jumped at the slightest noise. I had been crushed under the weight of that horrific nightmare. I was incredibly close to death that night; it still takes my breath away. The Verdes Cliffs was a place where I used to enjoy going to sit on the rocks overlooking the ocean and meditate about my life. The Verdes Cliffs had become associated with my nightmare.

I did not know if I could ever take the vision of what had happened there out of my mind. The force of those waves crashing against those huge rocks, the sounds of the ocean, the loud thunder, the lightning—all of that was a constant reminder of Eric's insanity. I did not know how long it would take for those images to fade from my psyche, but I knew God saw me through that period.

The seasons of time were fine threads that connected the days of my life. Swatches of years gone by had been carefully sewn into the chapters of my life. As I continued to sew my patchwork quilt, I had interwoven those delicate threads with that chapter of Eric and me. That, too, must be added to the continuum of my story.

CHAPTER 18

The Devil's Wrath

Life is so strange: the twists, turns, curves, bends, and those unexpected drops. At thirty-six, I looked back on life. I was so amazed I had come through without too many battle scars. There was no doubt I had some tiny splinters of the cross embedded in each of my shoulders. At times, I felt them. Thorns and thistles had surrounded me, and Eric had been one of them.

A life of bad choices, wrong turns, and impulsive decisions, repeated for years. I should have been more vigilant. Admittedly, one of my biggest problems was that I tended to quickly jump into a relationship based on a man's outward appearance instead of his heart.

When I saw Eric holding his Bible, I saw what I wanted to see. He was a well-respected man in his community and church, who carried himself as a gentleman. He introduced himself as a man of God, who was generous and well-mannered. Like a magnet, I was obviously drawn to him.

What a complete fool I was! The devil saw me coming.

Eric had bought me the world; he denied me nothing. A world of money, gifts, and elaborate living blinded me with materialistic things and caused me to see nothing, but what Eric wanted me to see.

Steady writing in my journals gave me the chance to express the feelings of my heart. With each word I wrote, tears fell from my eyes because I saw the many foolish mistakes I could have avoided if I had only stopped, looked, and listened.

God had been very good to me. Many times the Lord tried to stop me, but I moved too fast to notice, was too stubborn to hear, and was definitely one who hated taking advice. I prayed most of my life and learned to pray as far back as when I was a child living in a convent for three years. Since that time, prayer had become a big part of my life. Through the many roads I had traveled, my prayer life saw me through.

I was confused, disoriented, and unsure about the outcome of that chapter. The school of hard knocks had certainly been tough. It had been an encyclopedia of learning, the great atlas of time.

My life has been a world wide experience, full of extraordinary events. Good, bad, or indifferent, the process was well-worth the journey. I have heard nothing worth having comes easy. The emotional scars I had bore were a tribute to my determination to win, but it could have left a wasteful effect on my life.

Circumstances had the potential to make or break me, kick or shape me into a fighter. There was no doubt repercussions would be experienced that derailed me from living the life God had intended for me to live.

I had learned the roads I had traveled were for a purpose. As time moved on, I saw my character build, strength increase, faith grow, and outlook on life become much clearer and broader. My life had a purpose; I was not a mistake.

Traveling down the road I had been on was very scary, confusing, unpredictable, and frustrating. However, I had come through bad times before, and, with the grace of God, that chapter would come to an end as well. Yesterday was gone and nothing could be changed. All I could do was learn from the mistakes I had made and change my way of thinking in order to accomplish my goals and dreams.

I did not want to be stagnant nor do I want to fall off the edge. I wanted balance in my life, so when the hard times came, the scales would not tilt. I would be able to weather the storms.

Days passed, and I still lived on pins and needles, wondering if Eric would rear his ugly head. I stayed on the edge, especially as I worked my late shifts. Anytime after 10:00 pm, I would look for him.

One Friday night about 11:00 pm, my shift had run out because the relief driver had called in sick. I was on the Miller Street run—one of the worse lines in the division. Around midnight, I arrived at my layover. After I secured the bus, I walked over to Ferry Street to pick up a soda and chips. When I returned to the bus, on my seat laid black roses tied with black satin ribbons.

I had already been on a verge of a meltdown, and that discovery did not help matters. Eric was determined he was not going to stop. No matter where I went that man found me. I took the roses, threw them into the trash, and then I got back in my seat and took off.

That entire evening so many things happened. The railroad crossing gate was stuck, a passenger cursed me out, my fare box jammed up, and in the middle of all that, it started to rain cats and dogs. I finally arrived at the other end and got off the bus to use the restroom. When I returned to the bus, Eric sat in the front seat. I did not know what to do. Once again, I panicked.

"What's the matter, Mary, you look surprised!"

"Get off the bus, Eric!"

"Don't make me kill you here. You're pissing me off!"

I refused to board the bus. He stood up at the boarding platform as I stood at the bottom of the stairwell and looked up at him. I was saturated from head to toe.

"Get off, Eric . . . Get off now!"

"Do you really think you scare me?" he asked "Come on, Mary, one pull of the trigger and you're dead!"

In his right hand he held a gun and pointed it right at me. I wanted to grab the radio, but Eric was in the way. Rain came down in buckets, and thunder and lightning filled the sky; it looked like the Fourth of July.

I had little to no choice, so I got back on the bus. Eric started to back up slowly with the gun pointed directly at me.

"Do you really think you can run from me?"

I looked at him and all I saw was the blackness in his eyes and no color in his face. He looked like the walking dead.

"Eric, why are you doing this?"

The rain came down so hard I heard it pound on the roof of the bus.

"Eric, you're going to kill me over what?" I demanded an explanation.

He pulled back the hammer of the gun and I froze. I could not move, and all life seemed to drain from me. He cocked the gun again, and I slipped into another dimension. I could not scream.

"What's wrong, Mary, you look terrified! I thought you weren't afraid!"

This man is crazy; he's out of his mind.

"Eric, put the gun down . . . It's not worth it!"

"I loved you and gave you the world, and you betrayed me!" Eric shouted back.

I tried to maintain my composure, but my knees shook. Suddenly, he walked toward me as he pointed the gun at me and laughed.

"It's not funny, Eric, put the gun down!"

How terribly sad: that man was out of his mind, and I was caught up in the middle of his madness. I kept looking at him—I did not take my eyes off of him as he stood in front of me, an arm's length away.

"Eric, please put the gun down before someone gets hurt," I pleaded.

Unexpectedly, a street person approached the bus. I saw his shopping cart at the foot of the stairs. I did not turn my head in his direction, but slowly shifted my eyes toward where he stood. Eric noticed him at the same time.

"I'll be back," he said as he stood in front of me. "You haven't seen the last of me."

He walked off the bus. I turned to look down the stairwell and the other man was no longer there. My whole body felt numb. I looked around, but saw neither Eric nor the man; it was as though that man had vanished into thin air.

I could not catch my breath, and my heart pounded. I felt faint and the sensation of my legs was rubbery.

Another chapter in my life, another night I would never forget. Trapped between the pages of that horrible chapter, I almost lost my mind. When I arrived back at the division, I handed in my paperwork and went directly to my car. As I approached it, I stood in complete horror because on top of the hood lay black roses wrapped in plastic, tied with black satin ribbons.

"Where is he . . . Where is this man?" I shouted out, "Eric, where are you!"

I turned around in circles and walked up and down the parking structure, looking for him.

"Where is he? Where did he go? Where is that crazy man . . . Eric where are you?"

There was not a soul in sight, just bright lights, stars, and a quarter moon.

God he's not going to win!

I threw the roses into the trash can next to the huge white lamppost that lit the entire parking area. I got into my car and started the engine.

Oh, God, my gas tank is empty.

I pulled into a gas station near the corner of Vermont Avenue to get some gas. I went to the restroom, and then paid the clerk. I headed toward my car and as I opened the door I looked up. Eric's black Camaro was across the street with the headlights on: directed at me.

I quickly walked back into the mini-mart and asked the clerk to call the police. I stood inside the store and waited for them to arrive.

Suddenly, two police cars pulled up. As they stopped, Eric quickly pulled away. Once again I was left with no evidence he was stalking me. There was nothing I could say to the police because the escape artist was gone.

I found out the clerk never had a chance to call the police, so the officers had made a random appearance. I got into my car and drove off. Then, I heard a car horn blowing. When I looked up, Eric's black Camaro was directly behind me. He tailgated me and flashed his high beams to blind me. He kept honking his horn and blinking those lights—Eric had lost his mind.

My nerves were rattled. I tried to lose him. I drove to the entrance of the 91 Freeway, and when I turned onto it, Eric's black Camaro was directly behind me.

The rain came down so hard that visibility was almost at zero. I kept my eyes on the white lines on the road. Eric was on my tail, and I could not get rid of him. I tried to stay on the road.

Thank God the freeway was empty; not too many cars out there at 2:30 am.

Suddenly, his black Camaro turned off and disappeared. I pulled off on the shoulder of the road and opened my car door to vomit. I never felt that amount of fear before. Death was stalking me; the devil was coming for me.

I finally arrived home around 4:15 am. When I opened the front door, Arthur was sitting on the blue couch waiting for me. I told him everything that had happened. Then, I sobbed; I could not stop.

"This is ludicrous. We're going to the police!" Arthur snapped.

"Police? What? Do you see any bruises or scars? They can't do anything for me!"

As Arthur held me, I wondered if I would ever get the chance to start that new chapter of my life. I had anxiously waited for the opportunity for years to love and be loved. I was surrounded by the stillness of Arthur's love and wondered if my crazy nightmare would end.

I stayed awake the entire night and wondered if Eric would ever stop. I was up to my ears in twisted problems. I sat on the green chair by the dresser and looked out the window as I soul-searched for hours. I reflected on my life while Arthur prayed.

The many years of bad choices, wrong turns, and bad decisions landed me knee-deep in a pool of filth.

How did I get into this horrible mess?

What I had thought that night in Las Vegas foreshadowed what had transpired. When I saw Eric's change of behavior, I should have called it quits immediately.

For the next few weeks, Arthur rode with me on my bus runs. Of course, Eric did not show. I could not have a bodyguard for the rest of my life. So, after about three weeks, I was rode alone again.

Again, it was the calm before another storm; everything was quiet. There was no Eric, no Camaro, no nothing. In fact, I did not see black roses for quite a while. The man slithered in and out of my life like a snake.

I was taken off the Miller Street run and put back on the Avalon Boulevard bus line. I was shifted around so many times I had lost count. I sat on the edge of time and wondered what was going to happen? Time was slipping through my fingers.

Every page turned quickly through the chapters of time. I had lost sight of the contents. Eric Richards held me a prisoner and had me scared of my shadow. I was walking on a tightrope with no safety net beneath me.

Where I am in life? I can't even enjoy it.

Despite all my fears, Eric was not going to beat me. Driving a bus had left me wide open and made it easy for Eric to find me anywhere, anytime. There had been no boundaries or perimeters. I was open for the kill.

I rode up and down Avalon Boulevard, and everywhere I drove I looked for Eric. Every night was the same, but one particular night turned into a complete catastrophe.

I had checked my watch for the time; it was midnight. I pulled my bus into the layover, and then I walked to the drugstore on the corner. I returned to the bus and headed back to the garage. One block before Van Ness Avenue, Eric pulled his car directly in front of the bus and cut me off. I blew the horn and prayed someone had heard me.

"Get out of my way, Eric!" I shouted.

I called the dispatcher and told him I needed help. Within minutes, the bright lights of the transit police approached us.

Immediately, Eric turned his car around and drove off. When they reached my bus, Eric was gone as usual. Once again, I felt like prey without a predator. That boogeyman patiently crunched down and waited in the shadows to come in for the kill.

I drove into the yard and parked the bus. When I got off the bus, I looked around to see if Eric was anywhere. No sooner had I reached the double doors of the division had Eric pulled up in the front of the building.

"I'll get you! I'll see you soon, real soon. Mary!" he shouted.

I waited about an hour or so and got into my car. As I drove down Main Street, Eric followed behind me two car lengths. I turned into one street and down another in an attempt to lose him. When I got to a bridge, Eric cut his car directly in front of mine. I could not move; I was stuck. He opened his car door and walked toward me.

"I can kill you now, Mary, and throw you in the river! No one will know!"

My reaction was to blow the horn so someone would hear me. When I put my fist down, he grabbed my arm and stared at me.

"You made a fool of me, Mary. I should kill you right here and get it over with!"

How far will my mind take me before it splits?

Eric Thomas Richards was a man of many faces and no heart, feelings, or conscience. I looked straight into the eyes of the devil and saw the blackness of his soul. He projected his negative energy, hatred, and anger —the very core of what made that man tick. I saw death.

That gun he held was pointed directly at me. His eyes, that haunting stare, pierced through my soul.

I was trapped and he had me where he wanted me.

Now, what is he going to do?

My heart throbbed; it skipped several beats. My senses were slipping away. I looked into the gun barrel and saw bullets.

Oh, God, the gun is loaded!

Tears clouded my eye sight and rolled down my cheeks. Everything deep within that man was coming to the surface. I was totally helpless and at the mercy of his twisted mind.

"Eric, please stop before someone gets hurt"

He looked through me as though he did not see me. I knew something was very wrong with Eric. I heard the echoes of the past, small details came to mind, something so familiar.

I stood in my kitchen back in Caldwell Hills, and T. J. was drunk out of his mind. He screamed at me and was out of control. All his anger and hatred, all his bitterness was turned on me.

"I never loved you. I married you to get away from my father, I should kill you and get it over with!" he shouted.

The sounds of his fury bounced off the walls. I held my ears because the words he spoke were too hurtful to hear.

"I hate you. I should've never married you. I want a divorce!" He shouted as he shook me.

There I was. At seven and a half months pregnant, every bit of his anger and frustration was directed at me.

"I want out of this marriage. I don't want you or the kids. I want my freedom! Do you hear me, Mary? Do you hear me?"

"T. J., I'm pregnant. You're going to hurt the baby . . . Stop!"

That night had been an awful one. T. J. dragged me from room to room. Everything in his path, he kicked away.

"I hate you! I hate you! Do you hear me, Mary? I hate you!"

"No, the door . . . I'm going to fall, T. J.! Get back! God no!" I screamed.

I fell backwards down a flight of stairs and landed in the small vestibule next to the side porch door.

"I'm bleeding, T. J., help me, I'm bleeding!" I cried out.

I lay there with my knees to my chest and grimaced in pain.

"T. J., Mom, Dad, somebody help me!" I cried out.

There I was again, stuck within the chapters of a twisted man's mind; someone who never got out of his past. What was going to happen, I did not know.

Will he kill me, or will he let me go?

There was absolutely nowhere to go, no safety from Eric's madness. Twenty-five hundred miles from where it all began, and it looked as though I was losing the battle. T. J. Masterson would have a good laugh—what he had failed to accomplish to destroy me, Eric Thomas Richards would fulfill.

It's crazy. It's my life and people try to destroy it. They're determined to make my life a living hell.

I held on for dear life between life and death. I prayed for a miracle. Gigantic, raging tides had washed over me and tried to take me down. Their force was so powerful it almost ripped me apart. I quivered as I hung on with a shred of strength left in me. I fought for my life and prayed to make it to shore before the waves destroyed me.

A smoldering pot filled was filled with suppressed feelings, anger from the past. Eric Thomas Richards personified a scared mind, scorched from the hot irons of years gone by, which made him bitter and callous. Trauma had turned his heart to stone; whatever he touched, he destroyed.

He watched every move I made. I drove one of the worst lines of the division and was a sitting duck. Eric was obsessed and determined to control me; to have his way or die. I still had no idea why that man terrorized me.

Did I really want to date Eric Richards or was I trying to spite T. J. Masterson?

Shame on me; I had cut my nose off to spite my face and walked into the devil's trap. Instead of T. J.'s heart being pricked, I got stung. It was a long way up from where I had plunged. Before that grave overtook me, I had to climb out of it before it buried me alive.

Midnight was the darkest hour, the time when silence covered the earth. A time when sounds that were not apparent during the day came alive. Eerie, shrieking, shrilling sounds that took my breath away and brought the worse out of me—a paralyzing fear took hold of me, My nightmare stalked me. I was at the end of my sanity and my mind was about to split.

Night after night I watched my step, kept my eyes open, and became aware of my surroundings. In the darkest hours, that man wore many faces, dodged in and out of shadows, and slipped on and off my buses. In crowds he stood as quiet as a mouse and stared at me. That monstrous chapter was driving me out of my mind.

I was back on the Jefferson Boulevard line and knew Eric would find me. Most of his friends hung out in that area. I lived each night wondering when that man would strike. One particular night, Eric indeed struck.

I was coming off my run and waited for the relief driver by the train trestle by a funeral parlor next to Sherman's Florist. I stayed in the light and refused to stay on the bus. I remembered the many confrontations I had already experienced with that man. I was on thin ice and anticipated the ice would break at any moment and I would fall in. I was extremely nervous and my stomach was in knots.

God, where is this man?

I must have called the dispatcher three to four times to ask if my relief driver was on the way. Then, I saw James, Eric's organ player, pull up to the front of the nightclub across the street from the florist shop in his Mustang. He was directly across the street from where the bus was parked.

I did not know what to do, so I slowly backed up and stood behind a telephone pole to avoid being seen. From where I stood I heard all sorts of commotion, as people were everywhere, laughing and talking. I kept my eyes peeled in the direction of James' Mustang to watch for Eric to pop up.

Ten minutes had passed, and then thirty minutes. When I looked at my service watch, forty minutes had passed, and my relief driver was nowhere in sight. I called the dispatcher again and found out the shift was short drivers. I was so disgusted and frustrated; I wanted to go home. Where I was, was definitely not the place I wanted to be at that time. I quickly got back on the bus and changed my head sign. I tried not to be seen.

The night grew more intense, and every part of me felt as though I was being squeezed to death. I boarded the bus, started the engine, and as I was ready to pull off, police cars and paramedics raced by: I was stuck. I shut down the bus engine again. I was in plain sight, and not only were the interior lights of my bus on, but the external lights were lit as well.

In the middle of that commotion, Eric's black Camaro pulled up by the side entrance of the club. I got out of my seat and sat on the side seat to avoid being seen. There were crowds all over the place and in the middle of the crowd a couple hailed my bus.

Now attention will be drawn to me.

Not only did that couple get on the bus, but more people came along. As they boarded, Mike, Eric's bass player, was among the passengers

"Mary, what are you doing here? I thought you were up North!" he exclaimed.

He was so drunk he stumbled over his feet as he climbed the stairs. Mike was so out of it, he was loud and boisterous. He looked at me, but I do not think he was conscious of anything.

When I started to pull away from my stop, my relief driver flagged me down. I was so happy to see her. We exchanged places, and then I went back to the division, signed off, and went home.

That night was a close call, and I thanked God Eric did not see me. However, eight blocks before I reached the house, headlights approached me from behind. I tried to drive faster. I was so close to my destination. Just as quickly as those lights appeared, they disappeared.

Maybe it was my imagination. Maybe it wasn't him after all.

I was almost home, but had to stop at the railroad tracks for a train. When I made a left turn on Dorsey Street, the black Camaro came out of the alley and cut me off. Suddenly, Eric jumped out of his car and walked toward my car. He was drunk and loud.

"Mary, get out of the car . . . Don't make me hurt you!"

Someone has to hear this fool.

"Mary, we need to talk!"

I stayed in my car and would not move. I locked the car door and closed the windows. Eric was so outraged went back to his car, opened the trunk, and pulled out a lug wrench. Then, he headed toward my car again.

I was scared and my heart pounded, I could not catch my breath. I tried to start my car, but I was so nervous I flooded it: it would not start. The more I tired, the worse it became. As I looked at Eric I saw the fury in his face. I put my right arm over my eyes to protect them from shattered glass.

"Mary, open the door!" he shouted.

As he drew back his arms to break the window, a huge black and brown Rottweiler appeared, and growled and barked. Eric froze and slowly put down his arms. The dog was directly in front of him and looking at Eric as it showed its large K-9 teeth.

Eric was trapped. The dog did not move and continued to growl. I tried to start the car again: it started. I backed up my car and as the car moved, Eric turned to look at me. In that instance, the Rottweiler lunged forward and stopped Eric in his tracks. I pulled away. I looked in my rearview mirror and the dog had disappeared. All I saw was a dark figure of a man, staring my way.

I drove as fast as possible down Dorsey Street to Century Boulevard, and then to the apartment. I parked the car and went into the house. I was shaken up. I realized strange coincidences do not simply happen. God orchestrated them.

I had always believed angels existed; never once did I doubt they did. Throughout my life God had always been there for me. The Lord had never left my side. Once again, heaven opened up to me, angels had charged over me, and God's love poured down on me. What could have ended in disaster; the good Lord intervened to rescue me.

CHAPTER 19

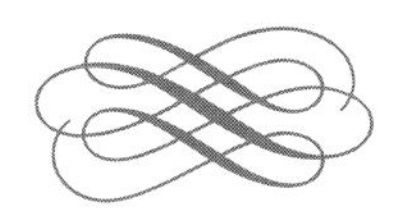

The Calm before the Storm

Arthur and I shared so much; our hearts had opened to one another. God knew exactly what He was doing. Even though there were times I did not quite understand, I knew God had my best interest at heart. The Lord had allowed me to travel twenty-five hundred miles to open doors for me. It was mind-boggling.

It was true; whenever I tried to play God, I always fell. It took me quite some time to realize God does not need my help. As soon as I stopped, things started to happen. The Lord had always looked out for me, even as a child knee-high to my mother's hip, God was there.

Many nights back on Essex Avenue, I lay in my bed and cuddled in the folds of my fluffy warm quilt. Sporty Beagle was at my feet, and Miss Molly snuggled in my arms as I talked to God.

I did not quite understand how God does things, but one thing was certain: all I was, all I ever would be, I owed to the Lord. I was much too old to chase rainbows. It was about time I grew up. So, I decided to let the Lord direct my life. Perhaps, I would get things right.

I was on my second lap. The race I was running had taken a new turn. As hard as things had been, I would make the proper adjustments and anticipate my future.

I had certainly made my share of mistakes, bad choices, and lots of wrong decisions. However, in spite of all the horrendous moves I made, much of me had grown stronger. What I was not able to do before, I felt quite confident of accomplishing them afterward.

Life with Arthur had gotten better. I opened up to him more. I shared my deepest secrets—ones I had not revealed to anyone. The dreams I thought were gone seemed to have revived.

God had made a way where there was no way. Much had come from all the mistakes I had made. There was a part of me that amazed me. I was not a shy, timid novice any longer. I had grown confident and strong; I knew what I wanted. Although that chapter of Eric and me seemed far from being over, if T. J. Masterson had not taken me out, then neither would Eric Richards.

Despite everything I had been through, Arthur and I spent a lot of time planning our wedding. Many days we would ride up the coast and park alongside the roadway to enjoy the beauty of the ocean so I had a chance to get away from Eric's madness.

Everything was so gorgeous: the whole scene looked like a huge watercolor painting. I had a great appreciation for life and embraced what I saw. Because of that, I viewed the world through the eyes of a child. I saw seagulls fly overhead—they circled the blue waters. How amazing it was to watch the brilliance of the sun shine down on the Pacific as it sparkled and looked like crystal teardrops bouncing off the ocean.

As uncertain as my life may have been, many nights I sat on the patio and meditated on God's goodness. I noticed the gorgeous jasmines by the huge, white, stone well flourish. Their fragrance was so delightful and strong that when I opened the windows and doors the scent accented the rooms, bringing spring alive throughout the entire house.

As happy as I was, it was difficult controlling my emotions. Some chapters of my life still brought tears to my eyes, particularly thoughts of my children and me. Everywhere I looked, I saw them and remembered the nights we sat in the living room on South Center Street as we colored, watched television, ate pizza, and sang "You Light up My Life."

Time had passed, but many broken chapters of my life still weighed heavily on my heart. The world taken from me seemed further away. All I had left were shattered pieces of my life. Tears saturated my pillow as I wondered if I would ever see my children again.

What happened to my dreams? They're all fading away, but I must believe they'll be restored one day.

The days were more beautiful and everything came alive. The green ivy climbed up the walls of the gazebo, which became hiding places for the little sparrows as they stayed out of each day's heat.

Nature's elegance was everywhere: the rainbow's brilliant colors; flowers alongside the wooden fence that surrounded the backyard; a huge terra-cotta burning, filled with wood; jam pots on the south side of the yard; and beautiful bird baths where birds gathered to take a leave from the midday sun. I loved the three-tier fountains as water cascaded down white stone buckets through the hands of angels into a huge basin.

It seemed as though I had walked back in time. Familiar scenes from my early childhood of Sporty Beagle chasing fireflies with Mama's glass jam jars and freeing them over the yellow daisies in the meadow next to our home.

My journals opened, and I waited to write a continuation of the story of my life. My mind was at peace, I was at rest, and I finally felt no fear.

What happens tomorrow, God only knows. I'm going to enjoy this peace while it lasts.

The clock on the mantel chimed at 3:00 am.

God where did the time fly? I'm so engrossed in this night and captivated by the peace that surrounds me. Thank you, Lord, for all You've done for me.

I transferred to the Foothill Division 60 miles away, but it was well-worth the effort. The area was beautiful, and everyone called it God's country because God's love was in constant motion. Burley mountains—sculptured caricatures—reached up toward beautiful blue skies. Everything seemed to be a masterpiece.

Everything was so different, calm, and peaceful; I felt like I was in another world. Up there so much innocence and simplicity existed that it took my breath away. I would sit on a little dirt hill that overlooked the countryside and was mesmerized by a babbling brook. I recalled a similar scene from my earlier years when Daddy and I skipped stones to the beat of nature's call.

How my mind wondered—I ended up anywhere my mind took me. From the open trails in the backwoods of Parsippany to the gorgeous elm trees in the midst of the red cobblestone paths next to Grandma Benning's farmhouse where the Rhode Island Red played with the ducks by the creek, for hours I would lose myself to escape from my life's madness.

Whatever it took, I definitely needed time to get my head back on straight. Far from where it all began, I was lost in a world of uncertainty, so I stayed where I was and enjoyed my walks down memory lane. I embraced whatever good memories came to mind.

It was quite a trek from Pomona to Los Angeles, but it gave me much needed distance from Eric Richards. Eric had become too much for me to deal with, and being so far away from him, I did not seem to have to look over my shoulders. It made a big difference in my life. Every moment of peace was music to my ears.

That horrible night on Verdes Cliffs as I stood on those slippery slopes was enough to blow my mind. I still woke up horrified. I would never forget that night nor the raging waters and ocean sounds. I was at the edge of death—the horrific thoughts and images drove me wild. I could not shake them or shrug off that nightmare.

I was in the calm before another storm. I knew I had not seen the last of Eric. I had been like a cat with nine lives; yet, the questions remained: how many lives did I have left?

God had always been good to me. Without a shadow of a doubt, if it had not been for the Lord, I would have been dead already. I was far from the end of my course. There were many questions left unanswered. Yet, I was not a quitter; I had never been known to give up. Come hell or high water, I was going to finish the race set before me to the end.

Days moved along quite nicely, and I spent most of them with Katie, a dear soul I had met when I first arrived in California. We would sit under the beautiful mulberry trees in her backyard, as I wrote pages about Arthur and me in my journals—how glorious those writing of incredible love were.

I felt like a schoolgirl as I wrote the feelings of my heart. I blushed at the words being written as I thought about falling in love. Who would have thought at my age God would open a door for me, and out of that door, came the love of my life. Only God alone could have made such a dream come into fruition. All the trying in the world, on my part, would have definitely failed.

When I stopped playing God, good things started to happen. The Lord was able to continue what he had started in my life. As long as I interfered, I stopped the hand of God.

I have so much to be grateful for because God had truly looked out for me. All I had gone through with T. J. Masterson, and I still came out on top. After ten long years of starting anew, I was starting all over again. I waited with great expectancy for the final outcome of my life.

I had been through hell and back and was not a novice anymore. I fought through the chapters of T. J. and me, survived the years of Uncle Jerry and me, and withstood the hardships of my mother and me. The chapter of Eric and me would pass, too. I would be free to go on with the story of my life.

I truly did not know how I survived it all. Physically, I made it through, but mentally and emotionally there remained many deep-rooted scars. Some of which were the splinters of the cross I carried. I appreciated my life and, although the years had been hard, I continued onward. What I had made out of life was what counted, and I could not allow anyone to take that from me.

It had been a long time since I had seen Rosie and Bill, or Jane and Earl. I had to write them, and one night I did just that. I lay across my bed and jotted down the feelings of my heart. I felt such a sadness with every word I wrote. Tears fell from my eyes as I remembered what we all had shared, and how one man had turned my life upside down.

Traveling back and forth from Pomona to Los Angeles took a lot out of me, but I stayed focused. My shifts were in the boondocks, which made matters worse. I could not count the times when I had made wrong turns. Getting back on schedule was another story.

The weather was much different than in South Bay. There were thunderstorms, and the winds were like mini tornadoes. I loved being in Pomona and prayed one day Arthur and I would buy a home there, in God's country. Perhaps, we would even have a small rescue team to care for the ones less likely to care for themselves.

Arthur and I had a lot of dreams. It did my heart good to know I could express my thoughts and feelings openly without fear of criticism or judgment. My life with him kept me going and made my days a lot less painful.

Eric had temporarily interrupted my life, and I hated it. When things had started to look up, I got entangled with a psychotic, twisted, troubled monster. He took great pride in doing what he did.

I really enjoyed my stay up with Katie and Jim in Pomona, but knew it was, in fact, temporary. I had to return to Los Angeles sooner or later to face that devil again. Until then, I made the best of what I needed to do and enjoyed the peace of mind it gave me.

I made friends with Katie's kittens; she had at least eighteen of them. They were adorable kitties of all kinds, colors, and sizes. I loved animals and watching them brought me great joy. Many days I sat out back and played with them as they climbed trees and scaled fences.

Over by a wheelbarrow, an eighteen year old, fluffy, white cat named Jeremiah lay on a sundial as well as a black cat and a golden brown tabby, Zoppriah and Joseph respectively. Leah and Isaac chased down Cheetoh, Katie's nine year old pit bull.

Chimes sounded as if angel's wings had touched them, cats meowed, and poor Cheetoh ran for his life. I sat in the midst of one of the most beautiful times of my life, surrounded by God's magnificent peace and love.

I felt like I was in another world; yet, I still had knots in my stomach. Every time I thought I had seen Eric, or simply heard the mention of his name, I fell apart. Strange, I could be in the center of a crowded room and the mere possibility Eric being near triggered my emotions. I knew I could not live the rest of my life running; Eric was not going to get the best of me. Somehow, someway, I had to find a way to overcome my fears. Running from him was not the answer.

Two weeks before Easter, my transfer back to LA Metro came through. I truly did not want to leave the Foothill Division, but I knew I could not hide from Eric any longer, so it was best to relocate. Nothing had changed; I was still on the midnight shift, which had become worse. I had little choice in the matter; it was either work or quit.

I held on to my prayers and faith in God as I clung to Arthurs love in my complex life. In spite of everything, Arthur and I still took trips to Venice Beach, walked around the pier, and enjoyed the quietness and peacefulness of Mother Nature's best. I was lost within those moments and realized how blessed I was because God was looking out for me.

"I love you, angel, my little colonial face doll," Arthur said.

I chuckled and blushed, and felt like a teenager all over again.

"I love you, too," I replied.

Arthur and I had made many plans for the future. For years I jotted down my dreams and goals, and being a passionate person, coupled up with the faith I held within me, I knew doors would open, roads would be paved, and ways would be cleared. Arthur and I would be victorious.

During my free time I enjoyed being in the midst of nature. I had always loved the colorful pallets of a rainbow. Even through the early years, I spent my days under the cheerfulness of a summer sky and enjoyed Mama's homemade goodies and Daddy's home-cooked surprises. I cherished those precious memories and locked them in the far corners of my mind to retrieve one-by-one to get through the seasons of my life.

My secret mental getaway was the calmness of the ocean hitting against huge rocks, the sweet smell of the ocean air, and the mist of waves touching my face—each brought such a peacefulness to my soul. Small things gave me a sense of hope as I reminisced on simpler and quieter seasons of my life.

I closed my eyes and still saw the tops of the Verdes Cliffs. I still heard the sounds of the ocean waves crash up against the enormous rocks. I had to get those hideous images out of my mind. Those Verdes Cliffs had left such an awful impression on my psyche. Often, I had to catch my breath, my heart raced, and I felt as though I was going to die.

"I hate Eric Richards!" I shouted.

That man messed with my mind. Where I go from there, I had no answer. I did not know how to get rid of that thorn in my side. My minds still played tricks on me. Even in the darkest shadow of the night, I still smelled fear all around me.

I finally had a weekend off after pulling a 10-day shift. I stayed home, took a shower, and sat in the gazebo as I hid from the rest of the world. Around eleven o'clock that night, I heard the clock on the mantel chime. Then, there was a sudden knock on the front door. I froze. I walked up to the door and looked through the peephole. A man in dark glasses stood on the other side of the door. I did not move or say a word. After a few more knocks on the door, the man left.

After a while, I finally opened the door. On the welcome mat lay a long white box tied with black satin ribbons.

"Oh, dear God!" I said aloud.

Black: Eric's signature color. Inside the box were a dozen black roses tied with more black satin ribbons. I cried so hard I could not catch my breath. My hands shook badly and my entire body felt like a piece of ice.

This is no way to live . . . I can't keep looking over my shoulders! How far will Eric take this? How far will this chapter go on . . . Will it ever end?

Fear crippled me once more. I was in a torture chamber: a dark, blackened, ice cold tomb with no way out. I had lived on the edge for years, poised to fall into an abyss. I thanked God that never happened. I knew fear was of the devil. It had been created from a discourage mind, a troubled heart, unraveling nerves, and a lifetime of shattered dreams. Fear had the potential to turn into depression, an emotion of nothingness.

From New Jersey to California, fear had chased me down and danger had followed me relentlessly. Ever since my childhood back on Essex Avenue, fear had lived within me and was perpetuated around me, especially as I watched my mother fall apart.

Visions of despair overwhelmed me as I remembered her standing over my brother's grave when she tried to kill herself. At barely seven years old, my mind did not comprehend what my eyes had seen. I watched my mother fall apart by his snowed over, sunken grave. That memory had never left me.

In the far corners of my mind, I knew since that day, a great part of my mother had died. It was a death that separated my mother and me forever. What had once been, no longer existed. I was on the edge of my life and prayed I would not wind up like she had.

I did not know the outcome of that chapter of Eric and me. I had no idea if that man was going to kill me or not. However, one thing I knew was I still resided in the land of the living and refused to give into my emotions and fears. I had to fight back and keep moving forward.

Where I had come from had not counted, but how I got through it was what really mattered. Having Arthur in my life had made all the difference in the world. I also learned an important lesson captured in the Bible, which reads: "Perfect love casts out fear."[5] God knew exactly what to do; I simply had to do keep believing someday my life would be victorious.

---

5 1 John 4:18, New King James Version (NKJV)

CHAPTER 20

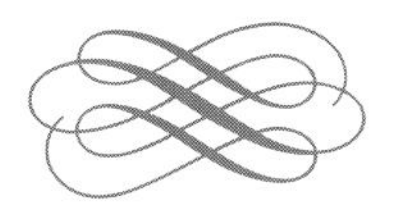

An Answer to a Prayer

I had been praying night and day for a miracle. Confused, frustrated, and simply beside myself, my emotions were out of control. I was still that little girl back on Essex Avenue, who cried her heart out. If only the walls of that big Victorian house could talk, what stories they would tell. When I reached into the far corners of my mind, I still shed tears because I never understood: *why me?*

There were still unanswered questions and so many unresolved issues left in my life. Twenty-five hundred miles from where it all began, and there were so many pages containing empty lines and chapters without words to express the feelings of my heart.

A million and one thoughts ran through my mind, and my emotions were still on fire. I had no answers to questions about chapters gone by. Everything remained clouded by disappointments and rejections. My heart still ached from all the hell I had gone through. Those pains from the past still echoed in my ear as I prayed to God for a miracle.

Life was so hard, and, as the pages of my life continued to turn, I prayed for a touch of hope, a smile, a hug, or maybe a memory or two that my mother truly loved me.

In the darkest, coldest night shadows, I still heard the silence in those long halls back on Essex Avenue. The echoes of nothingness still taunted me. Sixteen large rooms filled that house, yet in spite of the gorgeous antiques, and velour drapes tied with gold fringes, those rooms were barren. They had been void of my mother's love and affection.

For fifteen years I lived in that house and walked those halls. Throughout heart-wrenching nights, I did my best to hide from Uncle Jerry's madness and my mother's fury. I still hid in yet another season of madness and craziness. I had been trapped once more in the foolishness of all Eric's disguises.

Where's my mind? Trust what . . . Trust who? Why do I keep making bad choices? What's wrong with me?

That huge, monstrous mountain I had walked around still remained the same

Dear God, I can't seem to get out of this loop.

My heart continued to ache. Even at the end of my layover, I chocked back tears that had fallen. I felt so hurt, rejected, and unloved. As I looked for a light at the end of the tunnel, I saw absolutely nothing. I was walking with blind faith. In spite of how I felt, I still trusted God.

I had never given up. I had done many stupid things in my lifetime, but regardless of how bad things had gotten, God always caught me.

I had been so close to the edge, so close to that threshold of death; many a times I felt my foot slip. The distance from where I stood as I looked down a rocky slope was a long, hard fall. The distance between sanity to insanity had been a fine line.

"You're worthless! You should've never been born . . . You're a mistake . . . Everyone would've been better off without you! You're a stupid child . . . You're ugly . . . I should've killed you at birth! Why my sons died and you lived, I'll never know! No one loves you . . . No one cares for you! You're in the way . . . You're your Daddy's mistake and I'm stuck with you!"

I clutched my tiny cross and sobbed. Yet, I clung to God for my sanity as I awaited my miracle. The bridges I had crossed, the devils I had burned, and I sat on my bed wrapped in the folds of my quilt with nothing left of me, but a few precious memories.

I knew God loved me. Arthur had been good to me. He had been very patient with me. I was so mixed up, confused, and out of sorts. Yet, Arthur loved me anyway.

I did not know how to receive or feel love. I had asked myself so many questions. Can I move forward if I've never experienced real love? Where do I go? How do I escape this isolated, darkened tomb of nothingness? How do I open up to seek that love?

Arthur had truly been a gift from God. Being around him made me feel special. I embraced every syllable and clung onto every breath he took, Arthur was my guardian angel.

In spite of all the pain, I knew God was with me. Like that little girl back on Essex Avenue, I clung on to special moments and embraced the newfound life God had given me.

From Darkness to Dawn was where the Lord had taken me. I stood in full confidence that no matter what I went through, or the challenges I faced, God was not done with me yet. One day He would take me to a higher level.

Summer had arrived and everything was in full bloom. The birds gathered in the fullness of leaves in the gorgeous pine trees while butterflies danced to the melodies of tunes the little birds sang. The peak of each evening was the most delightful. On those hot nights, as the sun set over the mountaintops it gave off such a gorgeous, coral haze that illuminated the sky. Many evenings Arthur and I sat out back to enjoy it as we exchanged stories about our lives.

Everything seemed magnificent like a huge watercolor painting. It was nothing, but a heavenly vision of God's work in motion; His perfect work of creation. With everything that had happened in my life, I cherished those moments of tranquility.

I embraced the life God had given me and thanked Him every day for allowing me to get my life right. How that chapter of Eric Richards would end, I did not know. What would happen was still a mystery, but in spite of it all, I knew one day that road I had travelled would make a turn for the good. ,

Bitter or better, no matter what the devil had thrown at me, I promised myself I would never harden my heart or end my life. I owed so much to God. Even if I should live another hundred years or so, I could never repay God for all He had done for me. I was at the edge of time, on a very thin tightrope. As I walked along, I held on for dear life to God.

If anyone told me back how deep I would have to dig for my grace, I would have thought that person was crazy. Everything I had ever worked for, everything I had ever loved, and everything I had tried to achieve went up in smoke.

At the threshold of a new beginning, my feet would not budge. Arthur, bless his heart, sat patiently and waited. He encouraged and pushed me forward. I was dangling on a very thin thread over the side of that enormous rocky cliff.

I looked up at Arthur and said, "Arthur, please help me. Don't let me go."

How long will this crazy madness go on? How many more tears must I shed? How many fearful nights must I spend driving up and down those boulevards?

I was fighting for my life, survival, and sanity. The devil had not won and he never would. I had been in tighter situations and had confronted and fought many giants in my day. Rest assured, no matter how bad things may have looked, I knew God and I would win in the end.

That crazy man still stalked and threatened me. He thought he had all his *I's* dotted and *T's* crossed. That thorn in my side thought he had it all figured out. Eric truly believed he had me checkmated.

No matter how hard things seemed or how devastated, I was still in the land of the living. I had not travelled to California far on a magic carpet or ridden in on a white stallion with wings. I came on a wing and a prayer with hope of starting a new life.

Life must go on. Days and nights passed. The sun shone and winds blew. The rain fell where it would, and I, too, kept on going. I purposed to live every day one day at a time until my nightmare was over.

My life had been full of surprises. There had been many twists and turns; the roads I had travelled sometimes led into directions I had no business going. I never knew how difficult life could be.

I remembered as a young girl back on Essex Avenue I could not wait to grow up. As time passed, I wished it would stand still so I could regroup and catch my second wind.

Since stopping time was virtually impossible, I kept praying, moving forward, and my eyes on the cross. Since I had not gotten in that mess overnight, I would not get out of it quickly.

I had run off the deep end and jumped in way over my head. Perhaps, I lost my mind like I had back in the 1960s—somehow I always seemed wide open for hurt. My guard would drop: I had a mad rush to jump into the deepest end of the pool—head first—with absolutely no water beneath me.

If I lived my life over, I would probably make the same mistakes. It took my life to realize the seasons I had gone through were part of the learning process. Mistakes were tools God used to shape and mold my character. No matter how many times I stubbed my toe, I was a little stronger, a little better off than when I started.

T. J. Masterson and Eric Richards were men cut from the same cloth: smooth-tongued, charming, and hotheaded. From the age of thirteen to thirty-three, I had made a world of mistakes. In those twenty years, I had many close encounters with the devil. I made a promise to be more selective and cautious with my life.

I had done my best to watch my every step and not slip and fall, but every time my mind superseded my heart, good sense flew out the window. I was entrapped in that vicious web that had been weaved many years ago. God wanted to direct me, but I continued to direct myself.

I had many good friends to mentor me, but I was repeatedly entrapped. At thirty-something, I was still caught up in the moment and allowed the emotions of my heart to take control. As far back as Essex Avenue when I was trapped within those high sixteen rooms, I still desperately clawed my way out of trouble.

Loneliness has always been a great part of my life. Between the silence and emptiness of those enormous rooms, there was a thin line between sanity and insanity. Many times, I felt as though I was dead—I had entertained the thought of suicide many days. I fought off those desperate feelings as I walked those long halls on cold, winter nights, and listened to the winds enter the cracks of open windows and the chimney of the fireplaces in each bedroom—I prayed for a miracle.

In spite of it all, my memory was what kept me alive. My fondest memory was when Sporty Beagle and I cuddled upstairs in Mama's attic, wrapped in the folds of those old army blankets as we listened to the silence of the night. How I loved those evenings, especially on rainy, winter nights when the rain fell from the rooftops. We watched the raindrops dance to the sounds of the beating of my heart.

In the midst of the horrible chapter I was in, I closed my eyes and wished, if only for a moment, God would send me back to that particular time of my life. I missed my mother and father, and God knew how much I missed my dog. My heart truly ached, my eyes truly burned, and even though the years I spent with Mama were loveless, I still had an aching in my heart to see her face again.

Twenty-five hundred miles from where it all started, I felt truly homesick. God knew how much I missed the world I had left behind. I looked into the darkness and saw a full moon. The bright array of illuminating lights captivated the sky with beautiful shades of coral. I feel the peace of God surround me and wondered if I would ever see the other side of the rainbow.

I caught me smiling. It was awesomely remarkable to even imagine that moment was possible.

Pages had been turned in spite of that horrific chapter in my life. I had heard time had a way of healing all wounds; I doubted that occurred. My hands were tied, and what I wanted to do seemed virtually impossible. I could not seem to get back on track and was actually losing ground.

The dream my world would ever reunite seemed far from me. Coming to California had been a big move—I wanted to start a new life and give my family the home we never had. Twenty-five hundred miles from the world I loved, only God could connect that world with the one I was living, if only I had the patience to wait.

The ground I was standing on in California was different from ground I had stood on before. In spite of the miles between the two grounds, the only hope of happiness was the faith I had in God. I came to California on a wing and a prayer with great expectations for a better life.

I realized I could not do this with my strength, and I was definitely no match for the devil. My future lay in the palm of God's hand, and even though I was stuck between the pages of that nightmare, I believed wholeheartedly God was in control.

I was at the threshold of a new life. I had finally taken a step in the right direction. At thirty-something I was much too old to continue making the same mistakes. I knew the best was yet to come. Eric Richards, like T. J. Masterson, would one day be another part of chapters gone by in my life.

Those rough, hard, roads I had travelled made me stronger. Life was a continuation of seasons gone by and in order to experience growth, I had to embrace every opportunity those seasons brought.

Nothing lasts forever and, like that horrific nightmare of Eric and me, and one day I, too, would grow from the pages of life and be ever so grateful to God as I seized moments and reflected on what God had done for me.

CHAPTER 21

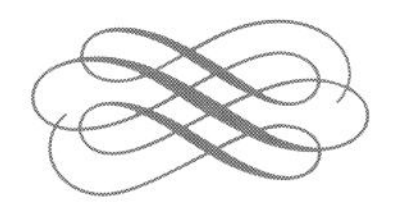

Enough Is Enough

As I stood on a threshold of a new life, I still could not seem to get it right. I would be foolish to allow the devil to destroy me. Eric Thomas Richards was not going to win. I blamed me for falling into another trap because I took my eyes off the Lord. I drove me closer to the edge. The desire to love and be loved was so palatable it consumed my mind, body, and soul to the point I made bad decisions.

The mind is a beautiful thing, but very dangerous. Good reasoning takes discipline and self-control, but when emotions get in the way, sensibility goes out the window. I had been going around the same mountain and it was quite depressing. I should have been wise enough to see trouble. I should have gone the other way instead of dodging the bullet.

Insecurity and weakness go hand in hand; I was all too familiar with that reality and quickly jumped into things I had no business jumping into. I had opened another can of worms containing nothing, but confusion, frustration, fear, and anxiety—a stream of emotional chaos had come of it.

Eric saw me and crafted a web that caught me, entangled me, and wrapped tightly around me. I had no means of escape. In my journals, I had written the feelings of my heart to search every part of me. I prayed for God to save me.

That horrific chapter had taken every ounce of life from me; it had worn me down to the bone. I feel absolutely stupid. Once again I had allowed me to go off track and be dragged into another distorted world. I allowed me to be raped of all my good senses. Shame on me to leave me wide open for hurt: I had vulnerability written all over my face, which exposed the weaker side of me.

It had been one year since I had met Eric down by the lake at Fielders Pond during a Sunday church picnic. What a glorious day that had been. I still saw the beautiful blue sky and smelled the plush, green grass. Hills of evergreen were everywhere, and in the lake I saw my reflection where the long neck white geese swam.

Eric seemed to be the man of my dreams; he was everything I had looked for, longed for, and desired. For hours, we sat on the grassy hill and looked down at the water. A feeling of peace came over me, and I embraced that moment so tenderly, not knowing I was setting myself up for another disaster.

The portrait before me was a painting of bad choices, wrong turns, and impulsive decisions. The painting had to change. Instead of defeat, I wanted victory written all over it; I wanted brilliant colors of peace, love, and joy. I wanted strong tones of hope and an extraordinary blend of awesome faith that could move mountains. I had to change my way of thinking and direct my thoughts in a more positive direction.

I'm too old to be so stupid.

May arrived and I counted down the days to our wedding. In spite of everything around me, I was not going to allow Eric Richards to rob me of that moment. Twenty-five hundred miles from where it all began, I still walked on rocky ground and tried to live with that situation as I sat on the edge of my seat.

My life had been one dramatic experience after another, a constant page turner, but the pages were blank without meaning. Many nights I sat in the gazebo and cried as I pondered if I would ever get out of that horrific nightmare.

Flashbacks of yesterday and scenes of my life still replayed in my mind. Memories overwhelmed me, some of which had even robbed me of moving forward. Overtaken by my penchant for failure and defeat, I fought for survival. I grasped for any shred of hope.

I wanted so much to put to rest those heart-wrenching chapters of my past. With expectancy, I wanted to push toward my field of dreams to make my life count for something. Filled with aspirations and excitement, I wanted to broaden my vision, think positive, and change my attitude.

Rattled by the emotions, I needed to find a more serene surrounding.

The water, that's where I'll go.

I got into my car and drove down to Playa del Rey. I needed to be alone with my thoughts and pray to God for my sanity. I sat for hours on the huge rock and looked toward the ocean. I was lost in the rippling of the water, watching the waves come up to the shore, and cradling my arms around my torso, listening to the sounds of the wind.

I was thankful that such a peace truly existed with a peace that took my breath away. I sensed the presence of the Lord. As a child in the arms of my Father, I rested in His peace. My life was like a chapter book, and I was lost between the written pages. As I sit on the huge rock, I was lost in thoughts of the goodness of God.

I had driven and pushed hard through any obstacle that had gotten in my way. I was truly blessed—God had looked out for me and had never left my side. I was a reflection of a crushed spirit and a broken heart; I had the wind knocked out of my sail. Yet, I had not been destroyed, so I should not have been counted out of that race.

I was determined to make something of my life. I knew God would pull me out of that nightmare and give me beauty for ashes. Those pages that kept turning, as horrifying as they were, would one day change course. I would be able to complete my story.

As I walked on the edge of time, I had to remember my goals and dreams, and not allow the clouds of life to distract me. Although the road before me was uncertain, I had come too far to turn back.

The life God had given to me I had somehow caused a detour to go the wrong way. However, those chapters, seasons, and sleepless nights were all a part of the building of my character. Although so many chapters remained unfinished, I had to continue to go on in order for God to make a stronger person out of me.

Every day was a new beginning, a new start. More doors were yet to be opened; more challenges were yet to be faced. Tired and very weary, if I tarried where I was, I would sink deeper in my mess, so I had to push forward. I had to press on until I felt solid ground underneath me. My plans continued and nothing was going to stop me, especially Eric Richards.

"Angel, are you all right?" Arthur asked.

The hell I was going through was evident. I saw the paleness in my face and sadness in my eyes. I always had a difficult time hiding my feelings. Time after time, I sat alone and tried hard to connect the dots and feverishly prayed to God to free me from the chains of the past.

Those days of years gone by were still heavy on my heart and weighed me down. I had tried to undo all God had done in my life.

"Are you really happy, angel?" Arthur asked. "When you cry, I cry. How can anyone hurt my little colonial doll face?"

I felt such sentiments like the ones Arthur expressed were very hard for me to take in. With all I had been through, words like his only made me put up my guard to protect me from any further hurt and disappointment.

I kept my distance and built walls around my heart. I even weaved a veil for my eyes to protect me from the realities of life. If I had exposed the true feelings of my heart, the world would see too much of me. That made me more vulnerable, open and subject to what I had tried to run from and set me up for further hurt.

I was tired of being the center of frustration and failure. The chains of my past prevented me from moving forward—they were destructive, discouraging, and held me back. Far The past still kept me in bondage. The enemy was doing his best to keep me from God's best.

I continued to work double shifts. New runs became available, and I took advantage of it. I did my best to stay away from Eric's madness. Between Hermosa Beach and Playa del Rey, I would sit by the water to enjoy my layovers as I watched the stillness of the night. Everything out there gave my spirit such peace and rest.

Whenever I wanted to escape from my everyday existence, I ran into my little world to hide and prayed to God for a miracle. The life I had lived had certainly been a hard and difficult one to say the least, but as overwhelming as it may have been I thank God every day for allowing me to go through that journey. Those were the chapters shaped me into the woman God intended me to become.

I sat in utter amazement and looked into the mirror. I saw a miracle, God's love for me. It reflected the true me: a lost, hidden child who desperately sought to be seen. With all that had happened around me, I tried my best to keep a positive attitude as I pursued better things in life.

Keeping in step took a lot of discipline. I was focused on God's promises. My determination and strong will to survive helped me to stay on course to keep my goals in front of me, my dreams with me, and run my race with a prayer in my heart.

A new chapter was about to be written, more storylines had to be told. Once again, I was in full gear; I pushed on and pressed forward as I aimed for my goal. I was excited and waited with great expectancy to read the ending of my story. I had such zeal and passion within me that I allowed God to be God and kept my hand to the plow. I disregarded what the enemy was doing and stayed on course.

I had waited so long for a day when I anticipated my new life as I flew high on the wings of God's love. My heart fluttered and my mind wondered. Yet, in the midst of my transformation a big part of me was still reluctant to give my heart away. I desperately tried to break loose from that madness and slowly pulled me out of that pit.

The walls I had built, the veil I had woven, had been for my protection. I had kept a close watch on my emotions, and a tight lid on my doubt and insecurities, because the events of the past had tried to cripple me and stunt my growth.

Those years being shut up within the four walls of that old Victorian house had almost driven me crazy. The past made an imprinted on my heart—a blistering wound. Chapters and of brokenness and despair, blank pages filled with nothingness, echoes of lost love—my mind, body, and soul still grieved.

A stillness cast over me as the child within me desperately tried to awaken from that life. My life experiences had already been more than in a normal lifetime. I tried to pick up pieces of what remained of me. My heart was uncertain, and my fears were very real as I clung to the One who had created me.

I refused to allow myself to think the worse. Those mixed emotions I felt, I refused to let them overwhelm or overtake me.

I will survive. I'll be victorious. I'm looking forward for the next hundred years, as I'm determined to win my race.

Days were growing longer, and the brightness of the sun was seen as it came over the mountaintops. Everywhere I looked, I saw God's love in motion. No matter how I felt even a small rose petal on the ground sparked my life, not to mention the sounds of newness around me.

I felt like a teenager once again. Bobby socks to stockings, I was on the threshold of a new beginning. Eric Richards had tried so hard to break and stop me from going forward. He tried his best to cripple me. Yet, I was more determined than ever to break loose from his madness.

I counted my blessing, as it was a miracle I had escaped his craziness. Running from the fear of living in the past again, I watched my footing because I knew if I kept moving forward, the devil could not take me down.

Twenty five hundred miles from where the nightmare had begun, I had learned nothing lasts forever. So, with that fact embedded on my heart, that period was also a part of the past, and a new season signaled another chapter had to be written. The continuation of my life's story would one day have a happy ending.

The weekend of our wedding had finally arrived. In the midst of confusion and uncertainty, I heard the sound of the wind blowing through the trees. The calmness of my spirit, even though I was still in the middle of another horrible situation, amazed me. I knew God had me in the palm of His hand. I knew I would survive. I still had no clue about how that chapter will end. Only hours before the wedding, and I still dealt with Eric's madness.

That Friday I worked a late shift. I still drove on the Manchester Avenue line, and the shift grew worse. Many nights my layover put me by a huge empty lot by abandoned factories. Never knowing where Eric would be was enough to blow my mind. My skin crawled from the fear of the inevitable. My stomach had sharp pains at the thought of walking so close to the edge. It nearly broke my sanity.

Being caught in the vicious web of another man's madness tore me apart. Whatever happened to that man had crippled him. Whoever he touched in his life, he destroyed. Unfortunately, being caught in the wake of his distorted mind, Eric was able to play with my sanity. A poor tortured soul—a part of me had empathy for him. Whatever had happened in his life had done him a great injustice.

Time was Eric's enemy, all those years he had lived his life it seemed he had lived it in pain. Although Eric and I were worlds apart, somehow those broken chapters I had written may as well be chapters Eric had written. Somewhere, in the course of time, in the deep pathway of life, Eric, too, was subject to someone else's madness. The difference between him and me was the will to survive.

Saturday arrived, and I finally had a reprieve from the craziness around me. I went to the mountains to spent time with Liza and Bob, some dear friends of Arthur's from when he was in the Marine Corps. I remember as a little girl I ran to my hiding place to get away from Mommy and me. Two decades later, I still ran from the madness of everyday life. I had travelled across miles of stretched highway; rode over dusty, hot roads; and gone over mountains and hillsides to get where I was.

It seemed I had been traveling all my life on a wing and a prayer. I had lived on God's good grace. Those long, dark, and dreary nights I looked out bus windows as I travelled West and saw my reflection stare back at me. God spoke to my heart as I soul-searched and tried to find a sense of calm and peace.

I clung to my metal cross and prayed to God for a miracle. I knew I had to go on. I could not and would not look back. I dug my heels in that much deeper and kept my eye steady on the cross. Every day I thanked God for the life He had given me.

I was truly persuaded the hand of God was always on me. The horror that stood before me would pass. Although the enemy tried to bring fear upon me, I knew and believed God was bigger than any situation or circumstance. The Lord was bigger than any giant I had ever seen.

I had to separate the new chapter of Arthur and me from past chapters. Fresh pages were about to be written and my pen was ready to write. The new chapters were destined to be the best chapters of my life. God had promised me beauty for ashes and He does not lie. I was embarking on a new adventure, a new beginning.

God was in control. The Lord was the One designing my life. Finally, I was excited and geared up. I was thrilled to start anew, and confident and secure in the decisions I was making. I knew God was directing me.

For the first time in a long time I opened up released the feelings of my heart. As I feared revealing too much, I still allowed me to be me. The tide was turning and I felt the change of the wind. There was much more peace in my heart.

The Manchester Boulevard bus line grew harder—the long, late hours were heartbreaking. At 2:30 pm, the parking was already horrible, which made it difficult to park. I was forced to park my car around the corner on Van Nuys Boulevard. At 3:00 pm, I started my shift. As I drove up and down Manchester Boulevard, there was no sign of Eric anywhere. About 7:00 pm, I stopped in front of the doughnut shop to pick up a hot chocolate. As I walked out the shop's door, Eric startled me.

"Eric, you scared me!" I shouted. "What do you want? What are you doing here?"

He did not say a word and showed not an ounce of emotion. He just passed me by as though I was not there. He went into the doughnut shop. I dropped my hot chocolate and ran to the bus and took off.

That night was so cold and rainy; visibility was very bad. Low clouds had come in from the harbor and thick clouds were so thick that seeing was virtually difficult. The stillness of that night sent chills up and down my spine. It was a though someone walked over my grave.

My shift had ended. As I walked up the street to my car, I felt the mist touch my face. The fog was extraordinary. All I heard was my heartbeat. I was scared to death.

Dong! Dong! Dong!

It was 11:00 pm and the feeling of fear crippled me. I sensed death was stalking me. I was agitated my feet could not move fast enough. Suddenly, as I turned the corner, I felt a dreadful sensation come over me—a cold, clammy feeling.

Those church bells sounded really loud; for some reason they had frightened me. My legs felt like lead. The faster I tried to walk, the slower I went. Suddenly, I heard noises come from behind. I quickly turned to see who it was, but as dark as it was I could not see a thing.

"What's that? Who's there!" I shouted.

I shook like a leaf and my heart was pounding.

No one is answering me.

"Who's there? Say something!" I shouted again.

I fumbled in my purse for my keys. I heard that sound again.

"Who's there!" I shouted.

The rain was coming down so hard I could not see a thing.

Where's the sound coming from?

"Mary, you can't run from me," the voice calmly said.

I was horrified. I did not know what would come next.

"If I can't have you, nobody else will have you," the voice whispered into my ear.

Through the thickness of that fog appeared the face of Eric Richards. He pinned my arms down to my sides and held them tightly. I struggled and tried to fight back, but he had such a tight hold on me, I could not move. Then, he pointed a gun at me.

"Don't make me kill you," he warned.

He had pinned me to the car, which was exactly where he wanted me. I was trapped. Eric could have killed me and no one would have known what had happened. Suddenly, he pressed his body against mine while his right hand lowered the gun to my side. Then, he raped me.

I could not scream because he was so strong and forceful. He kept his left hand over my mouth to prevent me from screaming. Not a word was spoken, there was a dead silence.

My legs trembled, and I felt my knees shake; I could not stop them. Time stood still. It seemed forever before Eric stopped. Tears ran down my face, but I still saw that unemotional, dark-eyed monster looking at me. Not a sound came from him. All his anger, frustration, everything came from within him. I was the very thing he used to take it all out on.

When it was over, Eric stood there with a blank look on his face. He had the gun pointed at me. Suddenly, a surge of strength came from within me. Something had happened, and I did not feel fear any longer. Standing in front of me was a man I had been running from for such a long time. Instead of running from him, I looked at him and all I felt was contempt toward him.

"Eric, I don't care anymore. Do what you want . . . Kill me . . . Whatever. I'm not running anymore. This is it!" I shouted.

He just looked at me. Not a word came out of his mouth.

"What's wrong, Eric? I'm not afraid of you anymore!"

For once in my life I felt those chains of fear loosen as boldness and strength came over me. Enough was enough. From a distance, those church bells struck midnight. I boldly turned myself around, picked up my purse, grabbed my keys, opened my car door, and started my car.

Eric just stood in the pouring rain, the darkness of the night and stared at me. The only sound heard were sirens from afar, dogs barking, and the rustling of leaves beside my car.

I did not see Eric Richards again. It was almost as if he had fallen off the face of the earth.

Like in *From Darkness to Dawn*[6,] I was stronger for that experience and thanked God every day for all He had brought me through.

I truly believe out of the worse chapters of our lives, some good can come out of them. We can overcome. It had only been through the grace of God I had proven I can survive.

D. H. Lawrence once wrote:

I never saw a wild thing

sorry for itself.

A small bird will drop frozen dead from a bough

without ever having felt sorry for itself.7

---

6 Adams, *From Darkness to Dawn.*

7 Lawrence, David Herbert. 1929. *Pansies: Poems. London: Martin Secker.*

God has been very good to me, I am truly blessed. I have finally seen the light at the end of the tunnel. As I lie in the folds of my quilt, listening to the wind blowing through the barren trees outside my bedroom window, I give God all the glory for another season of victory.

Epilogue

The world is a beautiful watercolor painting with all colors of the rainbow. Looking up toward the sky it is as if I am looking through a glass mirror, captivated and mesmerized by the glorious beauty of God's love. I stand on top of the world, looking at shades of blues and brilliant greens, pallets of golden yellows, and earth tones. As I glance over the mountain, I see a beautiful sight. What a privilege to be a part of God's creation!

I am standing on the threshold of a new beginning. As I continue this journey, I am forever grateful for what He has done for me. What the devil meant for evil, once again, God has turned it around for the good.

Today, as I stand in the midst of all this beauty. I am eternally grateful to God for His love, faithfulness, and mercy. The love I so longed for, the love I had prayed for, is mine now. Today, is the beginning of the rest of my life. As I look over this bright beautiful horizon, I know this time is forever.

Arthur and I will continue on this journey together. We'll live out our lives for Christ, as we journey our way home.

It is doubtful whether God can bless a man greatly until he has hurt deeply.[8]

—A. W. Tozer

---

8 Tozer, A.W. 1955. *The Root of the Righteous. Harrisburg, Pennsylvania: Christian Publications.*

For more information about

Mary Adams

&

Five Hours Before Midnight

please visit:

maryadamsauthor.wordpress.com
colonialdollface@yahoo.com
facebook.com/colonialdollface

For more information about
AMBASSADOR INTERNATIONAL
please visit:

www.ambassador-international.com
@AmbassadorIntl
www.facebook.com/AmbassadorIntl